St. Stanislaus

RECENT RESEARCHES IN MUSIC

A-R Editions publishes seven series of critical editions, spanning the history of Western music, American music, and oral traditions.

RECENT RESEARCHES IN THE MUSIC OF THE MIDDLE AGES AND EARLY RENAISSANCE
    Charles M. Atkinson, general editor

RECENT RESEARCHES IN THE MUSIC OF THE RENAISSANCE
    James Haar, general editor

RECENT RESEARCHES IN THE MUSIC OF THE BAROQUE ERA
    Christoph Wolff, general editor

RECENT RESEARCHES IN THE MUSIC OF THE CLASSICAL ERA
    Eugene K. Wolf, general editor

RECENT RESEARCHES IN THE MUSIC OF THE NINETEENTH AND EARLY TWENTIETH CENTURIES
    Rufus Hallmark, general editor

RECENT RESEARCHES IN AMERICAN MUSIC
    John M. Graziano, general editor

RECENT RESEARCHES IN THE ORAL TRADITIONS OF MUSIC
    Philip V. Bohlman, general editor

Each edition in *Recent Researches* is devoted to works by a single composer or to a single genre. The content is chosen for its high quality and historical importance, and each edition includes a substantial introduction and critical report. The music is engraved according to the highest standards of production using the proprietary software MusE, owned by Music|Notes.™

For information on establishing a standing order to any of our series, or for editorial guidelines on submitting proposals, please contact:

A-R Editions, Inc.
801 Deming Way
Madison, Wisconsin 53717

800 736-0070 (U.S. book orders)
608 836-9000 (phone)
608 831-8200 (fax)
http://www.areditions.com

RECENT RESEARCHES IN THE MUSIC OF THE NINETEENTH AND EARLY TWENTIETH CENTURIES, 26

Franz Liszt

St. Stanislaus

Scene 1, Two Polonaises, Scene 4

Edited by Paul Munson

A-R Editions, Inc.
Madison

A-R Editions, Inc., Madison, Wisconsin 53717
© 1998 by A-R Editions, Inc.

All rights reserved. No part of this book may be reproduced or transmitted in any form by any electronic or mechanical means (including photocopying, recording, or information storage and retrieval) without permission in writing from the publisher.

The purchase of this work does not convey the right to perform it in public, nor to make a recording of it for any purpose. Such permission must be obtained in advance from the publisher.

A-R Editions is pleased to support scholars and performers in their use of *Recent Researches* material for study or performance. Subscribers to any of the *Recent Researches* series, as well as patrons of subscribing institutions, are invited to apply for information about our "Copyright Sharing Policy."

Printed in the United States of America

ISBN 0-89579-406-3
ISSN 0193-5364

∞ The paper used in this publication meets the minimum requirements of the American National Standard for Information Sciences—Permanence of Paper for Printed Library Materials, ANSI Z39.48-1984.

Contents

Acknowledgments   vi

Introduction   vii
  Historical Background   vii
  The Music of the Edition   viii
  Notes   x

Texts and Translations   xi

Plates   xiv

St. Stanislaus

Scene 1   3
  Orchestral Introduction   3
  Chorus, "Qual und Leid!"   16
  Recitative, "Kindlein! Was weinet ihr?"   27
  Chorus, "Beschütz uns"   35
  Aria, "Mein Sohn, o still des Volkes Not" [Piano-Vocal Score]   42
Two Polonaises [Piano Scores]   53
  Polonaise 1   53
  Polonaise 2   57
Scene 4   71
  Orchestral Interlude, "Salve Polonia"   71
  Psalm 129, "De profundis"   156
  Chorus, "Salve Polonia"   167

Critical Report   193
  Sources   193
  Editorial Methods   194
  Critical Notes   195

Appendix: Libretto, Final Revision (1883), GSA 60/B3b   199

Acknowledgments

I wish to thank Mária Eckhardt, whose article on Liszt's "De profundis" whetted my appetite years ago to know more, and who alerted me in the spring of 1997 to the existence of the Hoffmann Deposit in Weimar; Evelyn Liepsch, my guide through the Liszt holdings of the Goethe- und Schiller-Archiv; Roland John Wiley, the superb advisor of the doctoral dissertation out of which this project grew; and Jane Elisabeth Munson, my wife, whose patience and encouragement considerably brightened the way.

Introduction

At the time of his death in 1886 Liszt was working on a project that had occupied his imagination for years, an oratorio on the martyrdom of St. Stanislaus. Liszt once called it his "Nunc dimittis," by which he meant a hymn for the close of day, a valedictory prayer, like the Canticle of Simeon.[1] Today *St. Stanislaus* is perhaps the least known of Liszt's major works, yet it raises some interesting questions. To the student of Liszt's aesthetics, the poetic form of the libretto appears as a surprising break from his published theory of oratorio, while, for a broader audience, the music invites attention as a monument of Liszt's late period. With manuscripts extant for two of its four scenes, *St. Stanislaus* represents the largest work written during the last two decades of his life. It allows us to hear, in one (albeit incomplete) score, the final developments of Liszt's compositional maturity, moving from the religious idiom of his Roman period with its synthesis of the modal and the chromatic (see, for example, the A-Phrygian opening of scene 1), to the austere dissonance of his prophetic late style (in the polonaises, the psalm, and the final chorus).

Historical Background

When Liszt moved from Weimar to Rome in 1861, he had plans for one last great creative project: the composition of religious music and, above all, the realization of a special vision for oratorio. "After having solved, as well as I could, the greater part of the *symphonic* task set before me in Germany, I mean now to fulfill the *oratorio* task.... For me, it is the one art-goal for which I have to sacrifice everything else."[2] In two essays published six years earlier, he had briefly outlined a theory of oratorio stating that the principal aim of the genre should be to inspire devotion and prayer and that, to this end, the authors of oratorios should employ a mode of representation analogous to epic (not dramatic) poetry.[3] Liszt put this theory into practice with *Die Legende von der heiligen Elisabeth* (1862), which he modeled on the medieval literary genre of hagiographic legend, and again with *Christus* (1866), for which he compiled a libretto from scriptural and liturgical texts that together present a "narrative" only indirectly, through the responses of biblical characters to the events of the gospels.

Sometime during Liszt's stay in Vienna between 25 March and 21 April 1869, he commissioned the Polish writer and folklorist Lucjan Siemieński for an oratorio libretto on the legend of St. Stanislaus, the eleventh-century bishop of Krakow martyred by King Boleslaus II.[4] The work was originally intended to be a companion piece to *Die Legende von der heiligen Elisabeth;* but, early on, the potential of the story for accommodating a certain political interpretation intrigued Liszt and led him to accept his librettist's understanding of *St. Stanislaus* as a dramatic—not devotional—oratorio. This was an entirely new direction and a form with which it appears that Liszt was not very comfortable. Years earlier, in 1855, he had considered the idea of dramatic oratorio to be a contradiction, for "the character of oratorio," he said, "is distinctly epic; lyric and dramatic elements can arise in it only episodically."[5] Now Liszt must have changed his mind, or else he used the generic title "oratorio" in a looser sense than before.[6]

Siemieński finished the libretto in the summer of 1869 and posted it in August to Liszt, who found it "fascinating."[7] The next year, Peter Cornelius prepared a German translation of a slightly revised version of Siemieński's Polish text.[8] Liszt began serious work on the music in the summer of 1874 but, troubled by what he came to view as deficiencies in the text, set aside the score after composing the first scene, "Der Schrei der Bedrückten." In addition to flaws in the poetry itself, Liszt disapproved of the unrelievedly negative portrayal of the villain, King Boleslaw,[9] on both literary and political grounds. Cornelius made some revisions at Liszt's request, but to no avail. He died on 26 October 1874, with Liszt still dissatisfied.

Thus began a protracted search for an acceptable text. Over the course of the next nine years Liszt engaged the services of at least five other poets: C. E. Blum von Hyrth (1875), Salomon von Mosenthal (1876), Franz von Dingelstedt (1878), "ein Fräulein G." (1879), and Karl Erdmann Edler (1880, 1883). Liszt's closest friend and counselor, the Princess Carolyne von Sayn-Wittgenstein, complicated the search by repeatedly challenging his literary instincts and insisting on the perfection of Cornelius's text: "In fact, it is not the poet that is lacking, but the musician. The poem works. But you do not believe in it."[10] In the end, Liszt stopped consulting her on the matter. A fresh versification of the libretto prepared by Edler in 1880 pleased Liszt very much. The last obstacle to Liszt's resuming composition of the oratorio was overcome in 1882, when he learned of an alternative version of the Stanislaus legend, in which the king is said to have repented of the murder. Following Liszt's instructions, Edler shortened his own 1880 adaptation of the libretto and transformed the ending to agree with the discovery. Delighted and inspired finally to possess a "definitive" text, Liszt began to work again on the score, but with some difficulty. These were the years of his famous late style, which did not lend itself to the large-scale structures required for dramatic oratorio. On top of this, his health was steadily deteriorating, and a cataract made reading and writing troublesome. During the last three and a half years of his life, Liszt completed the fourth scene: the interlude in the spring of 1884 and the last two numbers shortly before his death. No musical manuscripts survive for scenes 2 and 3.

What follows is a synopsis of Edler's 1883 libretto. The full text with translation is presented in the appendix of this volume.

Scene 1, "The Cry of the Oppressed." A crowd gathered in front of the cathedral in Krakow complains to the bishop, Stanislaus, about King Boleslaw's cruelty. The bishop declares that he will confront the king. The bishop's mother encourages him.

Scene 2, "The Royal Feast." As the king carouses with his men, Stanislaus appears to warn him of an imminent revolt and seizes the moment to rebuke him for his battle lust and the misery it causes his subjects. The king thanks the bishop for the warning but is angered by the rebuke. He falsely accuses Stanislaus of stealing a dead man's property. Rebels enter the hall by force and are repelled by the king's men. The bishop is wounded.

Scene 3, "The Miracle: Raising Petrus." The king presides in judgment over Stanislaus, who stands charged with legacy hunting. The dead man's heirs testify against the bishop in hopes of winning the property for themselves. God raises the dead man to testify to the truth: that the bishop had paid for the property. In a fit of passion, the king slays Stanislaus.

Scene 4, no title. An orchestral interlude describes the king's compunction and pilgrimage to a monastery in Carinthia. He sings a setting of the "De profundis" and joins a chorus to close the oratorio with the interjection, "Hail Poland!"

The Music of the Edition

It behooves those who perform or study an unfinished work to ask in what capacity it can stand alone as a satisfactory object for aesthetic contemplation. Can the completed sections be appreciated as autonomous pieces? Or does the composer's lapse into silence communicate a powerful message of its own, as in the struggle of Michelangelo's *Captives* or the paradoxically eloquent disarray of Pascal's *Pensées*? In the case of Liszt's *St. Stanislaus*, at least the first of these two questions can be answered in the affirmative. Liszt himself had the orchestral interlude published and performed on its own in 1884, and he intended for the psalm and final chorus to be paired in publication. (The cover sheet for the printer's manuscripts reads: "The final chorus with baritone solo, 'Salve Polonia,' follows the psalm without interruption.") In contrast to the manuscripts for scene 4, those for scene 1 can be considered incomplete, but only in two respects: they were composed in 1874 on texts (Cornelius's 1870 translation, plus the anonymous aria "Mein Sohn, o still des Volkes Not") that Liszt later rejected in favor of Edler's text, and the aria is extant only in piano score. There is no telling what changes Liszt would have made to the music in adapting it to the new libretto had he lived to do so. One would think he was planning only minor changes when he wrote to Marie von Hohenlohe in May 1880, telling her of plans to finish the oratorio in less than a year, "since about a hundred pages are already written."[11] That is, he had already composed the first scene years before. And yet, with this same letter, Liszt enclosed a manuscript for an entirely new beginning of the opening chorus, written just the previous day.[12] These caveats aside, it can be argued that the music Liszt composed in 1874 for scene 1 constitutes a whole. It sets forth the complete text of the scene as conceived by Liszt at the time, which approximates the text that he had in mind at his death. Sometime after 1874 several lines were added to the libretto near the end of the scene (see lines 43–54 in the appendix), but Liszt instructed Edler to cut them from the final revision.[13] It is unclear why Edler retained them.

The orchestral introduction (mm. 1–146) develops as the play between a Gregorian hymn for the Common of One Martyr at Vespers and Matins, "Deus tuorum militum," and a lament melody (emerging in mm. 23–26).[14] The people sing a chorus based on that melody ("Qual und Leid!", mm. 147–234), in which they complain of the king's abuses. The bishop hears them and decides to confront the king (recitative, mm. 235–343). The second chorus of the scene ("Beschütz uns," mm. 348–429) includes variations of both the Gregorian hymn and the lament melody.

Although the mother's aria is preserved in a manuscript (GSA 60/B3f) cataloged separately from the rest of scene 1, it is clearly meant to follow the chorus "Beschütz uns." Indeed, the verso of the last page of Liszt's piano score for that chorus is a draft of the beginning of the mother's aria. The aria unfolds almost entirely in E major and introduces two new themes: one associated with peace (mm. 73, 163, and 290) and one associated with love (mm. 118, 217, and 298). The mother charges her son, the bishop, to protect his flock. Her realization that he may have to die in that fight (chant melody, m. 189) leads to an exalted transformation of the love theme. Her earthly love (m. 118, "You rested under my heart") has its parallel in heaven (m. 218, "And tenderly they will press to their breasts / Their companion in everlasting delight").

The two polonaises subtitled "de l'oratorio St. Stanislas" are an enigma, for no version of the libretto calls for instrumental dance numbers.[15] This writer knows of only one reference to the polonaises in Liszt's correspondence. It occurs in his letter to Marie Hohenlohe of 11 January 1883: "I have already written the 'De profundis' and the [chorus] 'Salve Polonia,' as well as the preceding two polonaises: one quite lugubrious, the other triumphant."[16] But for the word "preceding," which seems to confirm they were part of the oratorio, one might interpret the polonaises as a kind of *Réminiscences de "St. Stanislas."* The first begins with a transformation of a theme heard initially at the bishop's entrance in scene 1 (see mm. 248–57, a kind of "bishop's theme," perhaps); the second closes with the melody of the Polish national anthem, *Jeszcze Polska nie zginęła* (sometimes called *Dąbrowski Mazurka*), which Liszt uses in the orchestral interlude. The polonaises survive only in a version for piano, and stylistically they resemble the other piano pieces of Liszt's last years.

The orchestral interlude, too, is mentioned in Liszt's letter of 11 January 1883: "Between the murder and the penitence at the monastery of Ossiach, I shall put an orchestral interlude narrating the pilgrimage of Boleslaus."[17] This he composed in the spring of 1884 as a major revision of a work he had written at Rome in 1863 but never published: a fantasia on two Polish national songs.[18] In an opening Andante pietoso originally based solely on the hymn *Boże, coś Polske* (O God, you who for so many ages have girded Poland with splendor of power and glory, . . . may it please you, Lord, to preserve [our] land and freedom!), he interwove the bishop's theme: see measures 1–16 and 87–110. The second part of the interlude is a setting of *Jeszcze Polska nie zginęła* (Poland has not fallen yet). Thus the progression of ideas begins with the king's approach to the church (bishop's theme) and God (the hymn) and ends with the rebirth of Poland (the national anthem). Liszt once claimed that "the sense of the whole work shines forth" in this number.[19]

Like the interlude, the "De profundis" was a revision of an earlier work: a setting for solo alto or bass dating from 1880–81. In reworking the psalm, Liszt assigned the vocal part to Boleslaw and added a male chorus (the brothers at the monastery?). The later setting is more elaborate than the earlier and includes some stunning harmony in the introduction and conclusion. The dissonance at measure 25 combines the opening intervals of the first two melodic phrases (F–E in mm. 1–2 and C–B in mm. 7–8). The melodic phrase that follows this dissonance, in measures 27–30, is a foreground reference to the larger passage's *Urlinie*, an ascent along Liszt's beloved "Hungarian" scale. At the heart of the "De profundis" is Liszt's lyrical setting of biblical verses 4 and 7, "But with you [Lord] there is forgiveness" and "for with the Lord there is mercy," the melody of which is related to the bishop's theme.

Lina Ramann's diary includes the following vignette from 31 May 1886:

"And *Stanislaus*?" I asked him at an opportune moment.

"Always this *Stanislaus*!" he cried, irritated and enraged, "leave me alone!" But immediately he lowered his voice and added, "That is not meant for you—but for all the busybodies, the snoops."

"Then Müller-Hartung gave me a false report," I interrupted.[20] "He wrote that he would be rehearsing the work in the spring."

"That's quite impossible. I cannot write a note." In his voice lay all the bitterness of his fate, all the sorrow it caused him. "Perhaps Gräfe will help me."[21]

Moved, I said nothing. After an interval he took up the subject again:

"I have finished the psalm for it, also the final chorus. They contain curious things—we had to show that we, too, have learned something." Now he enlarged upon the close of the work and, from time to time, hummed the words of the chorus, "Salve Polonia! Salve Polonia!"—his face and movements added to the effect—to me it was as if I were in a monastery, as if I heard monks passing through the cloisters, humming and murmuring their monotone prayers; I felt myself drawn into this last act of *Stanislaus*.[22]

Curious things indeed. The final chorus is an extraordinarily static work. The harmonic rhythm is slow, a tonic pedal point extends through the first forty-two measures, and dissonances are held so long they lose their acerbity.

These, then, are the manuscripts that we know Liszt completed and are extant. But were there others? Did Liszt complete music for *St. Stanislaus* that has been lost? Some of the manuscripts listed below under "Sources" did go astray after his death and were feared lost for some time. The evidence is inconclusive. Liszt never referred to completed music for scenes 2 and 3 *by title or text* in his letters, but he may have referred to it obliquely:

To Olga von Meyendorff, 20 November 1875: "The instrumental introduction and the two first scenes of the *St. Stanislaus* Oratorio are written. [Richard] Metzdorff has probably seen or heard them."[23]

To Carolyne von Sayn-Wittgenstein, 25 December 1882: "More than half the work is written out for piano (with voices); I must finish it, orchestrate it, correct it, and have copies made of it—this last job is more complicated than one thinks."[24]

To Marie von Hohenlohe, 11 January 1883: "There remains to compose the great scene of the miracle of the resurrection, in which the deceased owner of the field acquired by St. Stanislaus is called to testify."[25] Can we infer from this that "The Royal Feast" had already been composed?

At the least, Liszt formulated musical ideas for these scenes. In 1892 Franz Haberl recalled that, when they spoke together about the legend of St. Stanislaus, Liszt had especially delighted in the story of the resurrection, and that he had sketched for Haberl the "motifs and *Tonmalereien*" he intended to use.[26]

Notes

1. Liszt to Antal Augusz, 9 November 1869, *Franz Liszt's Briefe an Baron Anton Augusz: 1846–1878*, ed. Wilhelm von Csapó (Budapest: Friedr. Kilián's Nachf. königl. ung. Universitäts-Buchhandlung, 1911), 159.

2. "Nachdem ich die mir gestellte *symphonische* Aufgabe in Deutschland, so gut es vermochte, zum grösseren Theil gelöst habe, will ich nunmehr die *oratorische* (nebst einigen zu derselben in Bezug stehenden Werken) erfüllen.... Für mich ist es der einzige Kunst-Zweck, den ich anstreben muss und welchem ich alles Übrige zu opfern habe." Liszt to Franz Brendel, 8 November [1862], *Franz Liszt's Briefe*, ed. La Mara, 8 vols. (Leipzig: Breitkopf und Härtel, 1893–1905), 2:28.

3. See Franz Liszt, "Marx: *Die Musik im neunzehnten Jahrhundert*," *Neue Zeitschrift für Musik* 42 (1855): 228; and "Berlioz und seine Haroldsymphonie," *Neue Zeitschrift für Musik* 43 (1855): 52.

4. A much more detailed history of the work's composition can be found in my article, "The Librettos for Liszt's Oratorio *St Stanislaus*," *Music & Letters* 78 (1997): 532–50.

5. "Der Character des Oratoriums ist ausgeprägt episch; lyrische und dramatische Elemente können in ihm nur episodisch Platz greifen." Liszt, "Marx: *Die Musik im neunzehnten Jahrhundert*," 228.

6. This being said, it should also be noted that the parts of *St. Stanislaus* which Liszt completed were actually the *least* dramatic. Scene 4, especially, seems anticlimactic and long in the context of a drama. The structure is episodic; there is no dialogue (just Psalm 129 and the words "Hail Poland!") and no setting of the scene. However much *St. Stanislaus* evolved as a dramatic oratorio, at the end of the day Liszt drew his inspiration from the work's devotional potential.

7. "Le texte me passione." Liszt to Antal Augusz, 9 November 1869, *Liszt's Briefe an Baron Anton Augusz*, 159.

8. The revisions to the Polish text were made by a student of Liszt's, Count Władisław Tarnowski, under the supervision of Princess Carolyne von Sayn-Wittgenstein.

9. Although Cornelius and Edler used the German form of the bishop's name—Stanislaus instead of Stanisław—they retained the "-aw" in Bolesław.

10. "Au fond ce n'est pas le poète, c'est le musicien qui lui a fait défaut. Le poème marche. Mais v[ou]s n'y croyez pas." Wittgenstein to Liszt, 25 February 1877, Goethe- und Schiller-Archiv (hereafter cited as GSA) 59/48.

11. "Car une centaine de pages en sont déjà écrites." Liszt to Hohenlohe, 12 May 1880, copy in Hohenlohe's hand, GSA 60/B3m.

12. Thirty-two measures, "Weh uns! Der Schmerzen Schale voll zum Rande!" GSA 60/B3fl.

13. Liszt sent to him (through Marie Hohenlohe) the manuscript GSA 60/B3a marked with the necessary changes. Following the line "Dann suchen wir den letzten Schutz im Grabe," Liszt drew three parallel lines to indicate a cut.

14. The première of the orchestral introduction was performed, using the score prepared for this edition, on 29 September 1996 by the Adrian Symphony Orchestra with David Katz, conductor.

15. GSA 60/B3h. These should not be confused with the two polonaises in C minor and E major that Liszt published in 1852.

16. "J'ai déjà écrit le 'De profundis['] et le 'Salve Polonia'; aussi les deux polonaises précédentes, l'une fort lugubre, l'autre triomphale." Copy in Hohenlohe's hand, GSA 60/B3m. See also, later in the letter: "Pour le 4 Nov. [Carolyne von Sayn-Wittgenstein's name day] j'espère mettre à ses pieds, le partition terminée. Auparavant je ferai essayer probablement à Weimar, les deux polonaises, le 'De profundis' et le 'Salve Polonia.' "

17. "Entre le crime et la pénitence au couvent d'Ossiach, je mettrai un intermède orchestral, narrant le pèlerinage de Boleslas." Ibid.

18. The autograph for the earlier version is dated 11 December 1863 (Paris, Bibliothèque Nationale, ms. 153). However, Wittgenstein claimed in a letter to Adelheid von Schorn, 18 June 1884, that the arrangement of the first song (*Boże, coś Polske*) was composed in 1864 or 1865, and that the arrangement of the second (*Dabrowski Mazurka*) dated back to a stay at Bad Eilsen in 1850. Adelheid von Schorn, *Zwei Menschenalter: Erinnerungen und Briefe aus Weimar und Rome*, 2d ed. (Stuttgart: Greiner und Pfeiffer, 1913), 398. Perhaps there was some connection (or confusion) with Liszt's plans from around 1850 to write a Dabrowski movement for his projected Revolutionary Symphony.

19. "In dem Fragment (Orchester-Interludium), welches bei dar nächsten Tonkünstler-Versammlung hier aufgeführt wird, leuchtet der Sinn des ganzen Werkes hervor." Liszt to Otto Lessmann, 7 May 1884, *Liszt's Briefe*, 2:359–60.

20. Carl Müller-Hartung, kapellmeister at the Weimar Hoftheater and director of the Music School.

21. Alfred Gräfe, a professor at the University of Halle, planned to operate on Liszt's cataract in September 1886.

22. " 'Und der Stanislaus?' fragte ich ihn bei einer passenden Gelegenheit.
" 'Ewig dieser "Stanislaus"!' rief er gereizt und ingrimmig, 'laßt mich doch in Ruhe!' Sogleich aber fügte er ruhiger hinzu: 'Das gilt nicht Ihnen—sondern das gilt den vielen Neugierigen, den Schnüfflern—'
" 'Müller-Hartung hat mich dann falsch berichtet,' unterbrach ich ihn. 'Er schrieb mir, daß er im Frühjahr das Werk einstudire.'
" 'Ist ganz unmöglich. Ich kann ja keine Note schreiben.' In seiner Stimme lag die ganze Herbheit seines Geschicks, die ganze Trauer darüber. 'Gräfe hilft mir vielleicht.'
"Ergriffen, schwieg ich. Nach einer Pause nahm er den Gegenstand wieder auf:
" 'Den Psalm daraus habe ich beendet, auch den Schlußchor. Es sind curiose Sachen darin—wir mußten doch zeigen, daß wir auch etwas gelernt haben.' Nun breitete er sich über den Schluß des Werkes aus, summte die Worte des Chores dazwischen 'Salve Polonia! Salve Polonia!'—sein Gesicht, seine Bewegungen sprachen mit—mir war, als wäre ich in einem Kloster, als hörte ich Mönche die Kreuzgänge durchschreiten, ihre eintönigen Gebete summen und murmeln, ich fühlte mich hineingezogen in diesen letzten Akt des 'Stanislaus.' " Lina Ramann, *Lisztiana: Erinnerungen an Franz Liszt in Tagebuchblättern, Briefe und Dokumenten aus den Jahren 1873–1886/87*, ed. Arthur Seidl and Friedrich Schnapp (Mainz: Schott, 1983), 321–22.

23. *The Letters of Franz Liszt to Olga von Meyendorff, 1871–1886, in the Mildred Bliss Collection at Dumbarton Oaks*, trans. William Tyler (Washington, D.C.: Dumbarton Oaks, 1979), 214.

24. "Plus de la moitié de l'ouvrage est écrite pour piano (avec chant); reste à l'achever, à l'instrumenter, le corriger et en faire tirer les copies,—cette dernière besogne est plus compliquée qu'on ne pense." GSA 59/95.

25. "Reste à composer la grande scène du miracle de la résurrection, où le possesseur mort du champ acquis par St Stanislas, est appelé en témoignage." Copy in Hohenlohe's hand, GSA 60/B3m.

26. Haberl to Marie Lipsius (La Mara), 13 June 1892, GSA 59/398,1.

Texts and Translations

The bracketed title and stage directions for scene 1, although not found in the score, are common to all of Cornelius's and Edler's versions of the libretto.

[I Bild: Der Schrei der Bedrückten]

Deus tuorum milit[um]
Sors et corona praemium
Laudes canente[s] Martyris
Absolve nexu criminis

Chorus, "Qual und Leid!"
[Auf dem Berg Wawel vor den Thüren der Kathedrale.]
[VOLK]
Qual und Leid! O schnöder Tyrann,
Wüthest wie Pest im Lande!
Recht und Freiheit belegst du mit Bann,
Waltest mit Schmach und Schande!
Faustrecht herrschet; mit wilder Gier
Raubst du das Weib deinem Bürger,
Raubst ihm die Tochter, des Hauses Zier,
Mit der Schaar deiner Wür[ger.]
Thränen sind unser täglich Brod.
Angst unsre Sinne verwirrt.
Einziger Trost in Verzweiflung und Noth
Ist uns der Bischof, der Hirt.

Recitative, "Kindlein! Was weinet ihr?"
[Der Bischof erscheint in den geöffneten Thüren der Kathedrale.]
STANISLAUS
Kindlein! Was weinet ihr?
Was ist gescheh'n?

EINE STIMME
Sieh' uns ins Au[ge nur,]
Wirst uns versteh'n.

EINE ANDERE STIMME
Mir haben all mein Gut
Flammen verzehret.

[Scene 1: The Cry of the Oppressed]

O God, [you who are] of your soldiers
The portion, crown, and reward:
Them who sing the praises of your martyr
Absolve from the bondage of sin.

[At Castle Wawel before the doors of the cathedral.]
[THE PEOPLE]
Torment and sorrow! O contemptuous tyrant,
You rage in the land like the plague!
You banish justice and freedom
And rule with infamy!
Everyone fends for himself; with wild lust
You rob your subject of his wife,
You rob him of the daughter who adorns his house,
With the band of your stranglers.
Tears are our daily bread.
Fear confuses our senses.
Our only comfort in despair and need
Is the bishop, the shepherd.

[The bishop appears in the opened doors of the cathedral.]
STANISLAUS
My children! Why do you weep?
What has happened?

A VOICE
Just look in our eyes,
And you will understand.

ANOTHER VOICE
All my property
Flames have consumed.

EINE DRITTE STIMME
Mir ward mein Kind entführ[e]t,
Entführet, entehrt.

EIN GREIS
Mein Sohn ersehnt den Tod
Im Thurm, in Ketten.

[RITTER]
[Eilt herbei und kniet vor dem Bischof.]
Vater! Nur du kannst hier
Helfen und retten!
Boleslaw riss mein Weib
Fort von dannen!
Scheint noch der lichte Tag?
Schmettert kein Donnerschlag
Auf den Tyrannen?

STANISLAUS
Zum König eil' ich! Gottes Wort mein Schwer[t.]
Ich schaff euch Recht und Ende euren Kla[gen.]
Die Höll in ihm sei auf das Haupt geschlagen,
Dass nach des Kreuzes Frieden er begehrt.
Er soll nicht länger Gott zu trotzen wagen.

Chorus, "Beschütz uns"
[CHOR]
Beschütz uns o Vater! Einzig in der Welt
Verdanken Schutz wir deinem Hirtenstabe,
Wenn blut'ge Tyrannei den Sieg behält
Dann suchen wir den letzten Schutz im Grabe.

Aria, "Mein Sohn, o still des Volkes Not"
DES BISCHOFS MUTTER
Mein Sohn, o still
Des Volkes Not
Und bittre Thränen!
Du bist sein Hirt.
Der Wolf ihm droht
Mit gier'gen Zähnen.
Vor seinem Grimm
Und wilden Dräuh'n
Beschirm die Heerde!
Geh, Friedenssamen
Auszustreuen
In Polenlande!
Du ruhtest unter meinem Herzen;
In Liebe hab' ich dich gehegt,
Geboren dich in herben Schmerzen,
Und deiner Tag und Nacht gepflegt.
Dann hab ich dich, mein höchstes Erdenglück,
Freudig dem Dienst des Herrn geweiht;
So gebe seinem Volke Gott zurück
Durch dich die Friedensselig[keit.]
Und solltest du auch zahlen mit dem Leben
Als Zeuge der Gerechtigkeit,
So magst du nicht darab aus Furcht erbeben

A THIRD VOICE
My child was taken from me,
Taken from me, dishonored.

AN OLD MAN
My son longs for death
In the tower, in chains.

[KNIGHT]
[Approaches in haste and kneels before the bishop.]
Father! Only you can here
Help and save!
Boleslaw snatched my wife
Away!
Shines yet the light of day?
Does no thunder crash
On the tyrant?

STANISLAUS
I will hasten to the king! God's word as my sword.
I will bring about justice and the end of your laments.
May Hell in him be fully vanquished,
That he may desire the peace of the cross.
No longer shall he dare to defy God.

[CHORUS]
Protect us, O Father! Our only protection in the world
Is your shepherd's crook;
If bloody tyranny should triumph
Then we will seek ultimate protection in the grave.

THE BISHOP'S MOTHER
My son, oh still
The anguish of the people
And their bitter tears!
You are their shepherd.
The wolf threatens them
With greedy teeth.
From his wrath
And ferocious menace
Protect the flock!
Go, seeds of peace
To sow
In Poland!
You rested under my heart;
In love I protected you,
Gave birth to you in bitter pain,
And day and night cared for you.
Then you, my greatest earthly happiness,
I joyfully devoted to the service of the Lord;
So may God give back to his people
Through you the blessing of peace.
And should you also pay with your life
As a witness for justice,
From then on you should not tremble with fear

In heil'gen Kampf und kühnen Streit.
Des Himmels Hallen dann öffnen sich:
D'raus Heil'ge wallen zu grüssen dich.
Und innig drücken an ihre Brust
Sie den Genossen der ew'gen Lust.
Dann Heil dir! (du) tapfer Held des Herrn,
Des Polen Schirm und Hoffnungs Stern!

Psalm 129, "De profundis"
De profundis clamavi ad te, Domine,
Domine exaudi vocem meam!
Fiant aures tuae interdentes
in vocem deprecationis meae.
Si iniquitates observaveris Domine,
quis sustinebit? Quis sustinebit?
Quia apud te propitiatio est,
et propter legem tuam
sustinui te Domine.
Sustinuit anima mea in verbo ejus
speravit anima mea, anima mea speravit.
A custodia matutina usque ad noctem
speret Israel in Domino,
quia apud Dominum misericordia,
et copiosa apud eum redemptio
et ipse redimet Israel
ex omnibus iniquitatibus ejus.
Ipse, ipse redimet, et ipse redimet.

Chorus, "Salve Polonia"
Salve Polonia!

In holy battle and bold strife.
The halls of Heaven will open:
Thence saints will march to greet you.
And tenderly they will press to their breast
Their companion in everlasting delight.
Then hail to you! brave hero of the Lord,
Poland's protector, and star of hope.

Out of the depths I have cried to you, Lord;
Lord hear my voice!
Let your ears be attentive
to the voice of my supplication.
If you should mark iniquities, Lord,
who will stand? Who will stand?
But with you there is forgiveness,
and because of your law
I have waited for you, Lord.
My soul has waited in his word;
my soul has hoped, my soul has hoped.
From the morning watch until night
let Israel hope in the Lord,
for with the Lord there is mercy,
and with him there is plentiful redemption,
and he himself shall redeem Israel
from all its iniquities.
He himself, he shall redeem, and he himself shall redeem.

Hail Poland!

Plate 1. Franz Liszt, *St. Stanislaus,* introduction, autograph of full score (GSA 60/B3d), first page. Reproduced by permission of the Stiftung Weimarer Klassik.

Plate 2. Franz Liszt, *St. Stanislaus,* chorus, "Salve Polonia," autograph (GSA 60/B3r), first page. Reproduced by permission of the Stiftung Weimarer Klassik.

St. Stanislaus

VOICES

Chorus
Soprano (S)
Alto (A)
Tenor (T)
Bass (B)

Characters
Stanislaus (Scene 1 only)—Baritone
Boleslaw (Scene 4 only)—Baritone
The Bishop's Mother (Scene 1 only)—Mezzo-soprano
Oppressed Subjects of the King (Scene 1 only)—3 Mezzo-sopranos, 1 Baritone, 1 Bass

INSTRUMENTS (ORCHESTRATED NUMBERS)

Piccolo (Picc.)
Flute (Fl.) 1, 2
Oboe (Ob.) 1, 2
English Horn (Engl. Hn.) (Scene 1 only)
Clarinet (Cl.) 1, 2
Bassoon (Bn.) 1, 2
Horn (Hn.) 1, 2
Horn (Hn.) 3, 4
Trumpet (Tpt.) 1, 2
Tenor Trombone (T. Trb.) 1, 2
Bass Trombone (B. Trb.)
Tuba (Tb.)
Triangle (Trgl.) (Scene 4 only)
Cymbals (Cym.) (Scene 4 only)
Snare Drum (Sn. Drum) (Scene 4 only)
Bass Drum (B. Drum) (Scene 4 only)
Timpani (Timp.)
Organ (Org.) (Scene 4 only)
Violin (Vn.) 1
Violin (Vn.) 2
Viola (Va.)
Violoncello (Vc.)
Contrabass (Cb.)

Scene 1
Orchestral Introduction
Chorus, "Qual und Leid!"
Recitative, "Kindlein! Was weinet ihr?"
Chorus, "Beschütz uns"

19

187
Picc.
Fl. 1, 2
[a 2]
Ob. 1, 2
[a 2]
Bn. 1, 2
Hn. 1, 2 in F
Hn. 3, 4 in F
Tpt. 1, 2 in F
[1]
T. Trb. 1, 2
B. Trb. Tb.
S
-ger, raubst ihm die Toch-ter, des Hau-ses Zier, mit der Schaar dei-ner Wür-
A
-ger, raubst ihm die Toch-ter, des Hau-ses Zier, mit der Schaar dei-ner Wür-
T
-ger, raubst ihm die Toch-ter, des Hau-ses Zier, mit der Schaar dei-ner Wür-
B
-ger, raubst ihm die Toch-ter, des Hau-ses Zier, mit der Schaar dei-ner Wür-
Vn. 1
tr
tr
Vn. 2
Va.
Vc.
Cb.

21

22

23

24

25

216
S
A
T
B
Vn. 1
Vn. 2
Va.
Vc.
Cb.
Ein-
Ein-
mp
[zusammen]
geteilt
222
- zig- er Trost in Ver- zweif- - lung und
Ein- - zig- er Trost in Ver- zweif- lung und

27

244
Cl. 1, 2 in B♭
Bn. 1, 2
Hn. 1, 2 in F
B. Trb. Tb.
Timp.
Vn. 1
Vn. 2
Va.
Vc.
Cb.
[1]
gedämpft
zusammen
251
Cl. 1, 2 in B♭
Bn. 1, 2
Hn. 1, 2 in F
Vn. 1
Vn. 2
Va.
Vc.
Cb.

Langsam
STANISLAUS [BARITON]
lang
Kind- lein! Was wei- net ihr? Was ist ge- scheh'n?
Langsam
lang
Ob. 1, 2
sf
Cl. 1, 2 in B♭
sf
a 2
Bn. 1, 2
sf
EINE STIMME (MEZZOSOPRAN)
[lang]
Sieh' uns ins Au- [ge nur,] wirst uns ver- steh'n.
Engl. Hn.
EINE ANDERE STIMME (MEZZOSOPRAN)
Mir ha- ben all mein Gut Flam- men ver- zeh- ret.
Ob. 1, 2
Cl. 1, 2 in B♭
Bn. 1, 2
Ritenuto
Ob. 1, 2
sf
Cl. 1, 2 in B♭
sf
Bn. 1, 2
sf
f
EINE DRITTE STIMME (MEZZOSOPRAN)
Mir ward mein Kind ent- füh- r[e]t, ent- füh- ret, ent- ehrt.

278
Cl. 1, 2 in B♭
Bn. 1, 2
[a 2]
EIN GREIS (BASS)
Mein Sohn
mit Dämpfer
Vn. 1
Vn. 2
[mit Dämpfer]
[mit Dämpfer]
Va.
283
er- sehnt den Tod im Thurm, in Ket- ten.
[ohne Dämpfer]
[ohne Dämpfer]
[ohne Dämpfer]
Vc.
Cb.
286
[RITTER] (BARITON)
Va- ter! Nur du kannst hier hel- fen und

31

Schmet- tert kein Don- ner- schlag auf den Ty- ran- - nen?

*Der Dirigent wird gebeten nicht die 3/4 eifrig zu schlagen, sondern nur das erste Viertel ruhig anzugeben.

34

sei ___ auf das Haupt ___ ge- schla- gen, dass ___ nach des Kreu-

- zes Frie- - den er be- gehrt.

Er soll nicht län- ger Gott zu trot- zen wa-

35

365
S
Welt ver- dan- ken Schutz wir dei- nem Hir- ten- sta- - -
A
Welt ver- dan- ken Schutz wir dei- nem Hir- ten- sta- - -
T1
Welt ver- dan- ken Schutz wir dei- nem Hir- ten- sta- - -
T2
Welt ver- dan- ken Schutz wir dei- nem Hir- ten- sta- - -
B1
Welt ver- dan- ken Schutz wir dei- nem Hir- - - ten- sta-
B2
Welt ver- dan- ken Schutz wir dei- nem Hir- - - ten- sta-
373
S
-be, ver- dan- ken wir Schutz
A
-be, ver- dan- ken wir Schutz
T1
-be, ver- dan- ken wir Schutz
T2
-be.
B1
-be, ver- dan- - ken wir Schutz
B2
-be.
382
S
dei- nem Hir- - ten- stab. Be-
A
dei- nem Hir- - ten- stab. Be-
T1
dei nem Hir- - ten- stab. Be-
T2
B1
ein- zig dei- - nem Hir- - ten- stab. Be-
B2

37

rit.
Langsamer
399
Ob. 1, 2
Engl. Hn.
Cl. 1, 2 in A
Bn. 1, 2
Hn. 1, 2 in E
Hn. 3, 4 in E
T. Trb. 1, 2
S
A
T1
T2
B1
B2
[a 2]
ff
-ter! Wenn blut'- ge Ty- ran- nei den Sieg be- hält

405
Ob. 1, 2
Engl. Hn.
Cl. 1, 2 in A
Bn. 1, 2
Hn. 1, 2 in E
Hn. 3, 4 in E
T. Trb. 1, 2
S
A
T1
T2
B1
B2
dann su- chen wir den letz- ten Schutz im

412
[a 2]
Ob. 1, 2
Engl. Hn.
[a 2]
Cl. 1, 2 in A
[a 2]
Bn. 1, 2
a 2
Hn. 1, 2 in E
Hn. 3, 4 in E
T. Trb. 1, 2
p
B. Trb. Tb.
p
S
Gra- - be, im Gra- - -
A
Gra- - be, im Gra- - -
T1
Gra- - be, im Gra- - -
T2
Gra- - be, im Gra- - -
B1
Gra- - be, im Gra- - -
B2
Gra- - be, im Gra- - -

*See critical note for measures 422–28.

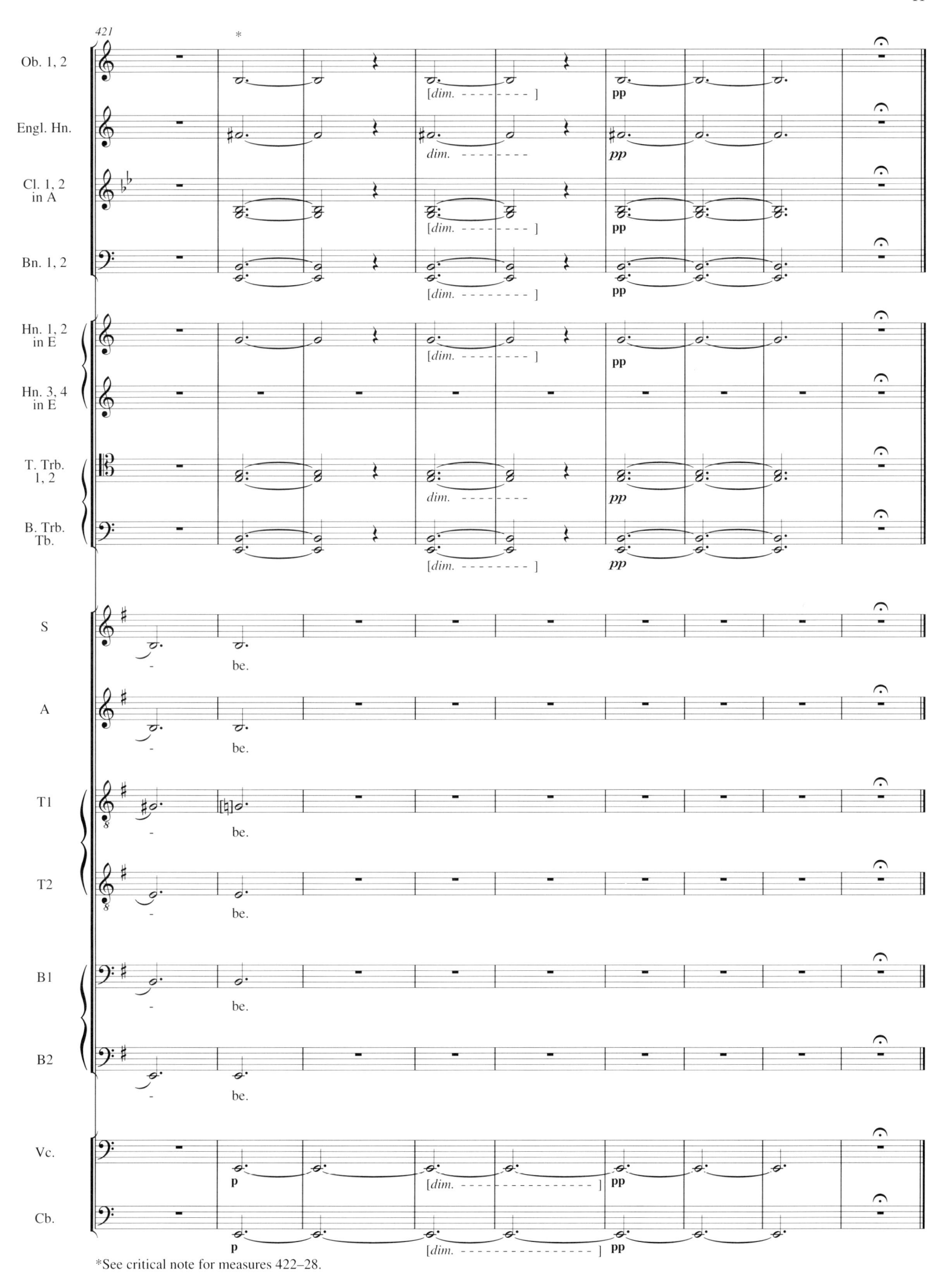

Aria, "Mein Sohn, o still des Volkes Not"

Un poco più mosso

Adagio (die Achtel nur ein klein wenig schneller als vorher die Viertel)

DES BISCHOFS MUTTER

Mein Sohn, mein Sohn, o still des Volkes Not und bitt're Thränen! Du bist sein Hirt, du bist sein Hirt. Der Wolf ihm droht mit gier'gen Zähnen. Vor seinem Grimm und wilden

Dräuh'n be- schirm die Heer- de, be- schirm die Heer- de, be- schirm die Heer- de! Geh, Frie- dens- sa- men aus- zu- streu- en in Po- len- lan- de!

Geh, Frie- dens- sa- men aus- zu- streu- en in Po- len- lan- de, in Po- len- lan- de, in Po- len- lan- - de!

Du ruh- test

46

unter meinem Herzen; in Liebe hab' ich dich gehegt, geboren dich in herben Schmerzen, und deiner Tag und Nacht gepflegt. Dann hab ich dich, mein höchstes Erdenglück, freudig dem Dienst des Herrn ge-

-weiht; so ge- be
sei- nem Vol- ke Gott zu- rück durch
dich
dich, durch dich
die
die Frie- dens- se- lig- [keit.]

Und soll- - test du auch zah- len mit dem Le- ben als Zeu- ge der Ge- rech- - tig- keit, __ so magst du __ nicht dar- ab aus Furcht er- be- ben in heil' __ gen Kampf __ und küh- nen Streit.

Des Him- mels Hal-

-len dann öff- nen sich: d'raus Heil'- -ge wal- len zu grüs- sen dich, zu grüs- sen dich. Und in- nig drük- ken an ih- re Brust sie den Ge- -nos- sen der ew'- gen Lust. In- nig drük- ken an

50

ih- re Brust _____ sie den Ge- nos- sen der ew'- gen Lust. _____ Dann Heil dir! Dann [Heil dir!] tap- fer Held ____ des Herrn, _____ des Po- len Schirm ____ und Hoff- nungs Stern! _____

Heil dir! du tap- fer Held des Herrn! Heil dir! du tap- fer Held des Herrn, des Po- - - len Schirm und Hoff- - nungs [Stern!]

Molto Lento (die Viertel wie früher die drei Viertel)

Two Polonaises

Polonaise 1

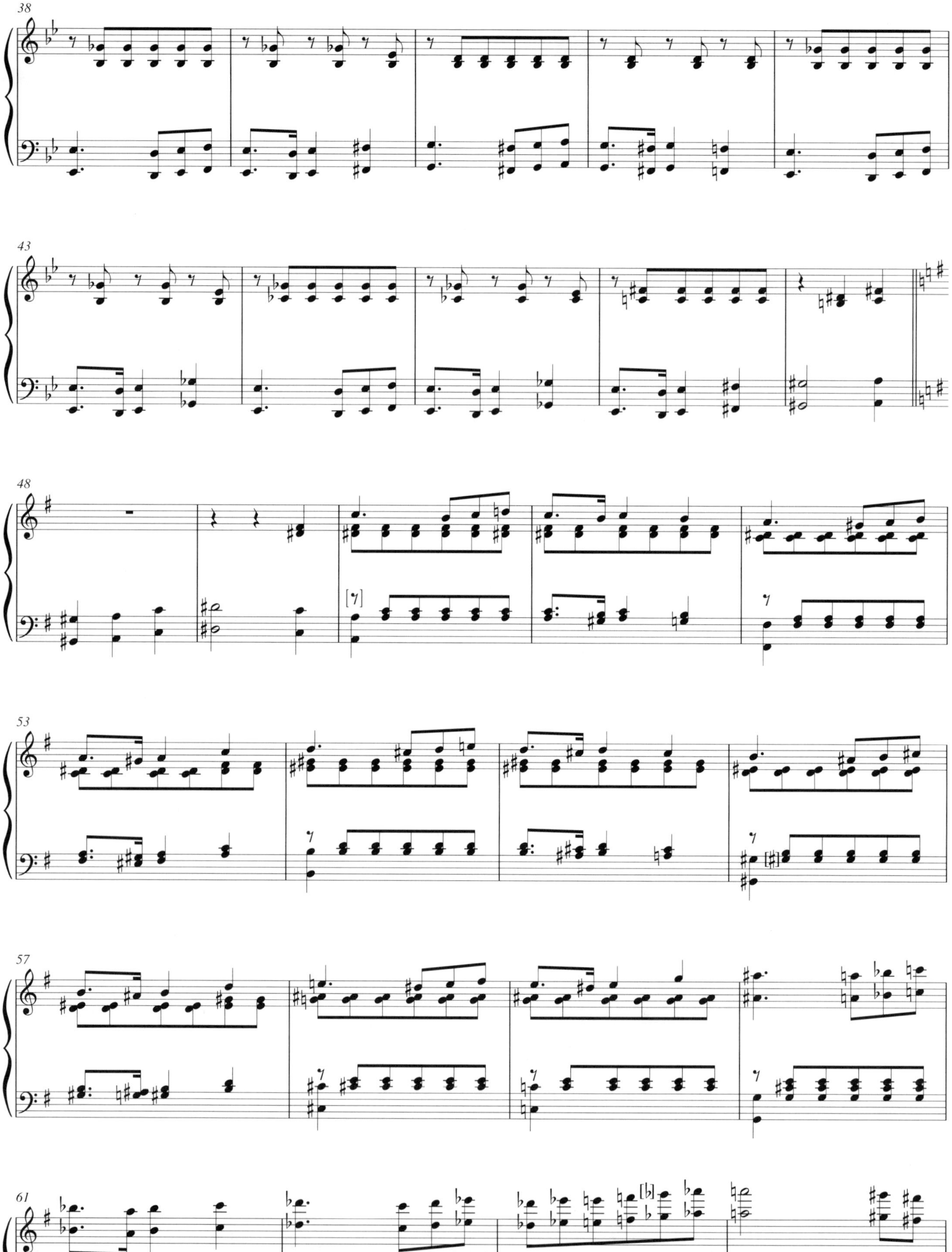
38
43
48
[𝄾]
53
[♮]
57
61
[♭]

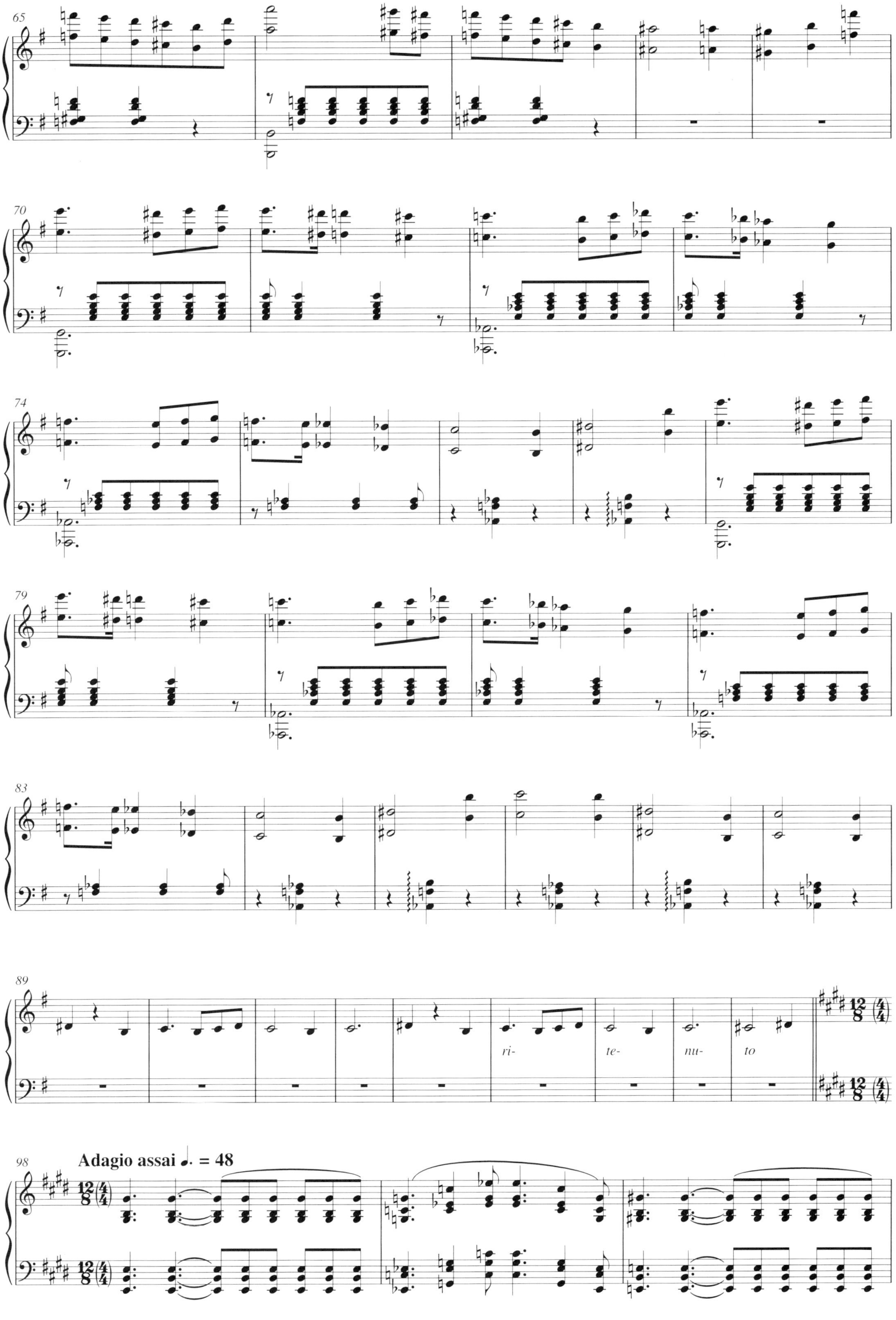
65
70
74
79
83
89
ri- te- nu- to
98
Adagio assai ♩. = 48

Suit Polonaise 2 (fa).

Polonaise 2

Allegro pomposo ♩ = 104

58

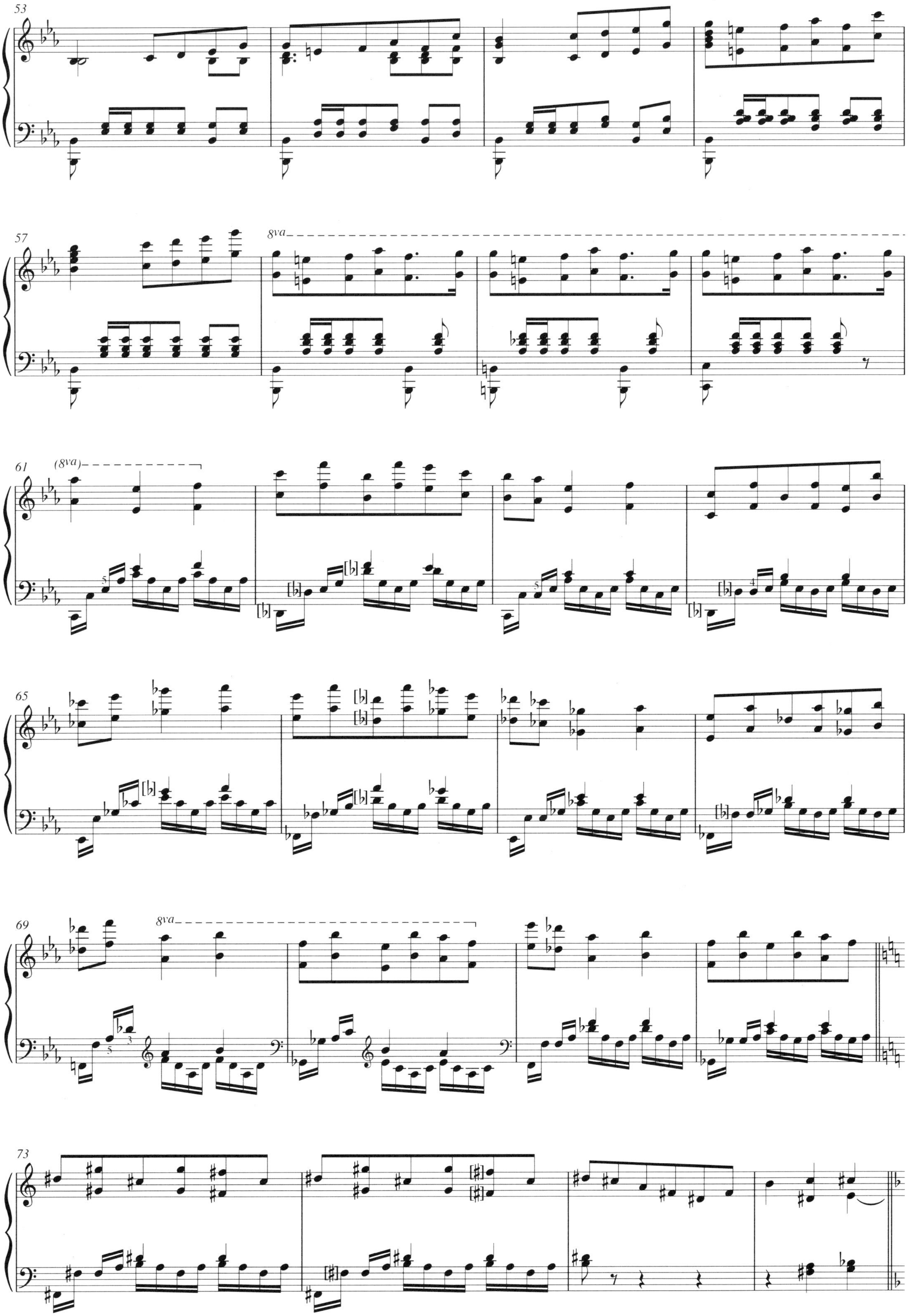
53
57
8va
61
(8va)
65
69
8va
73

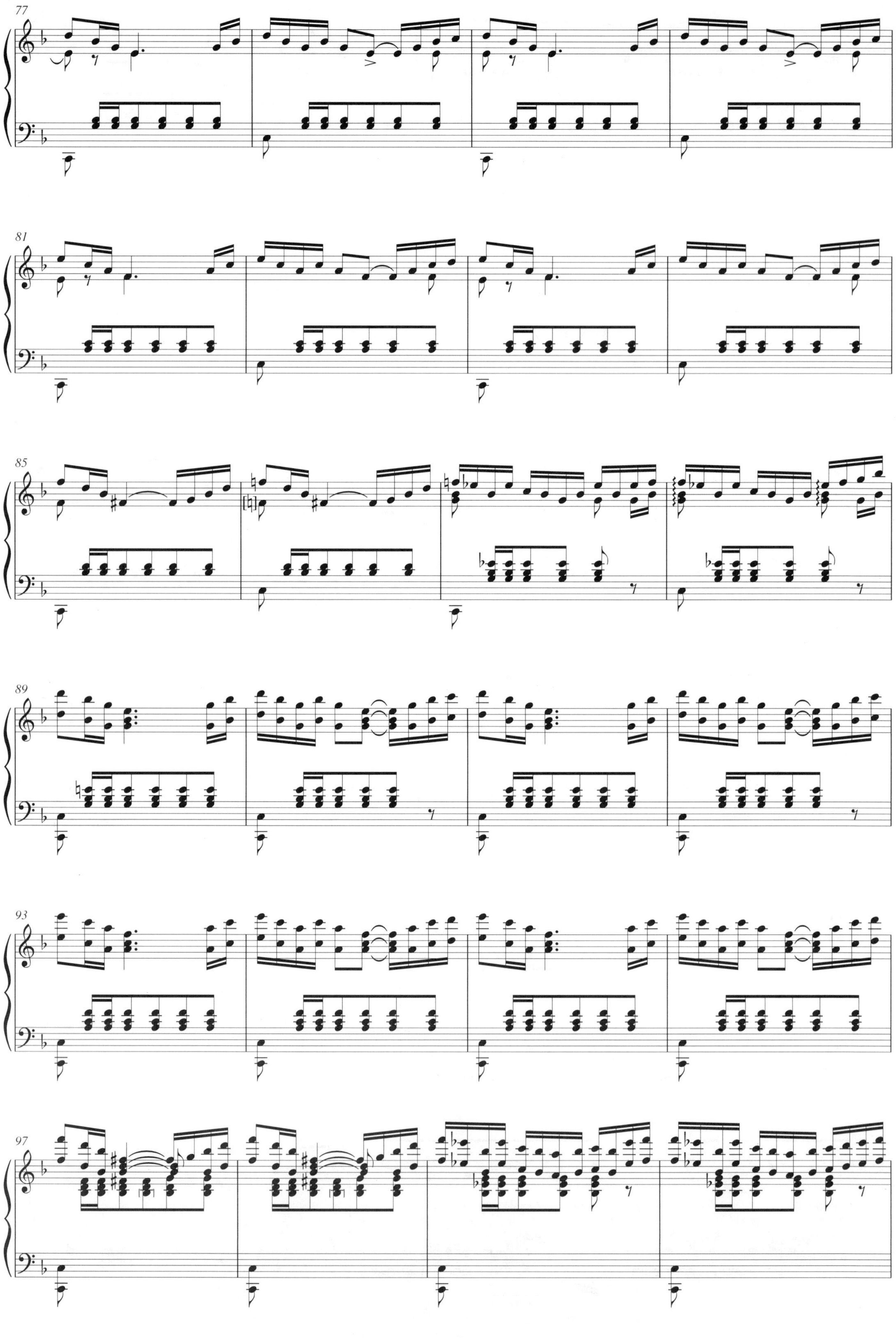
77
81
85
89
93
97

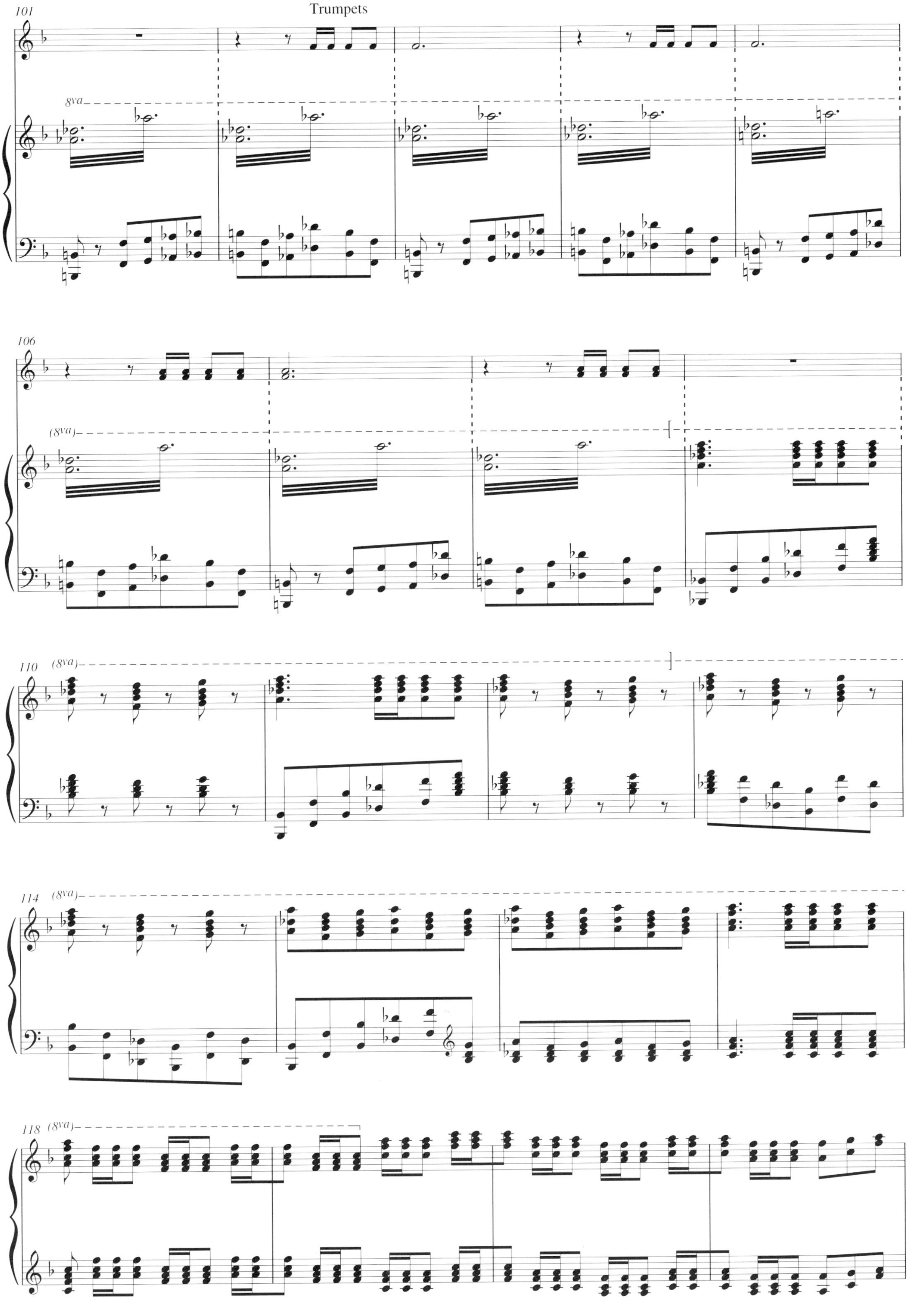
101
Trumpets
8va
106
(8va)
110
(8va)
114
(8va)
118
(8va)

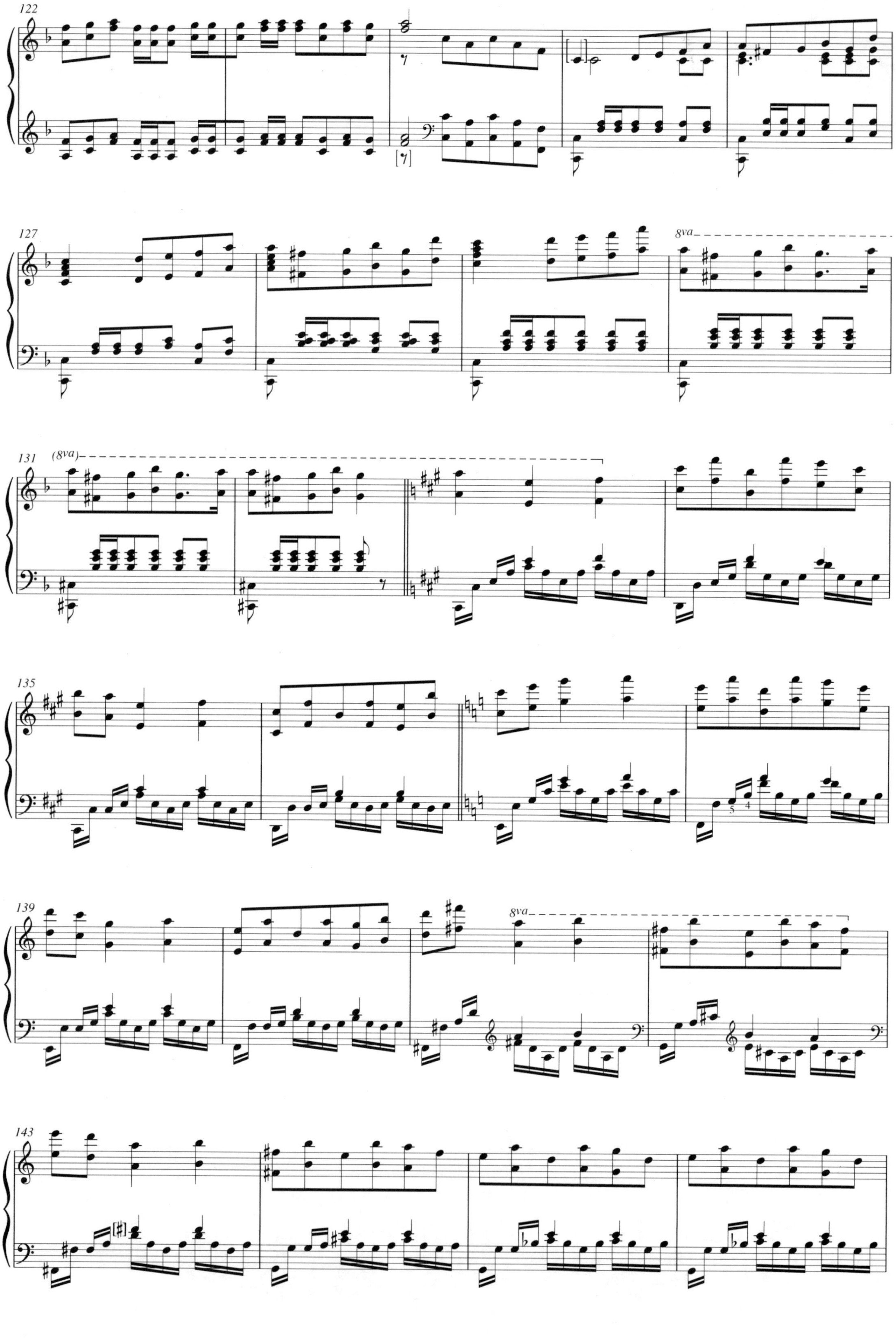
122
127
8va
131
(8va)
135
139
8va
143

63

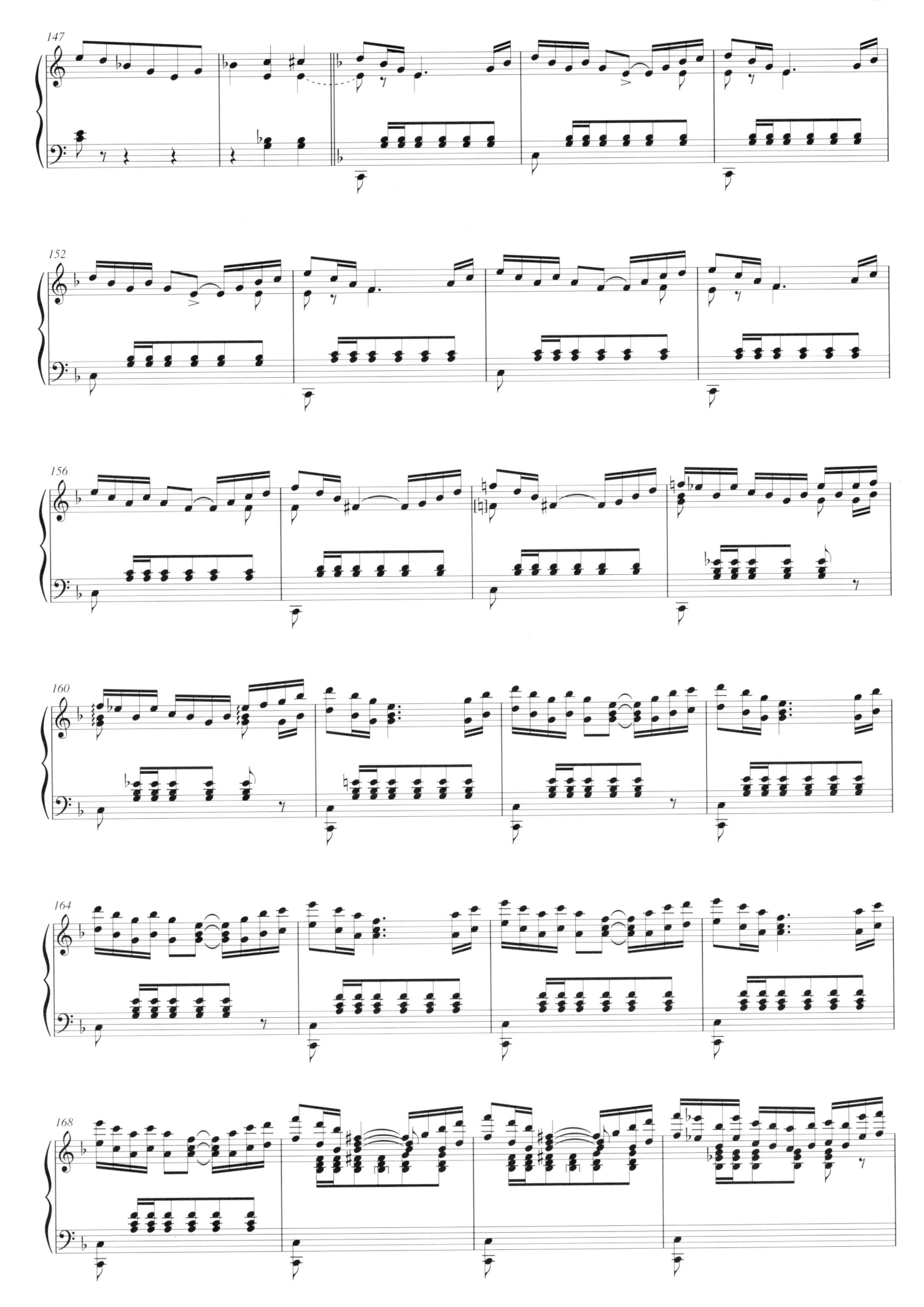

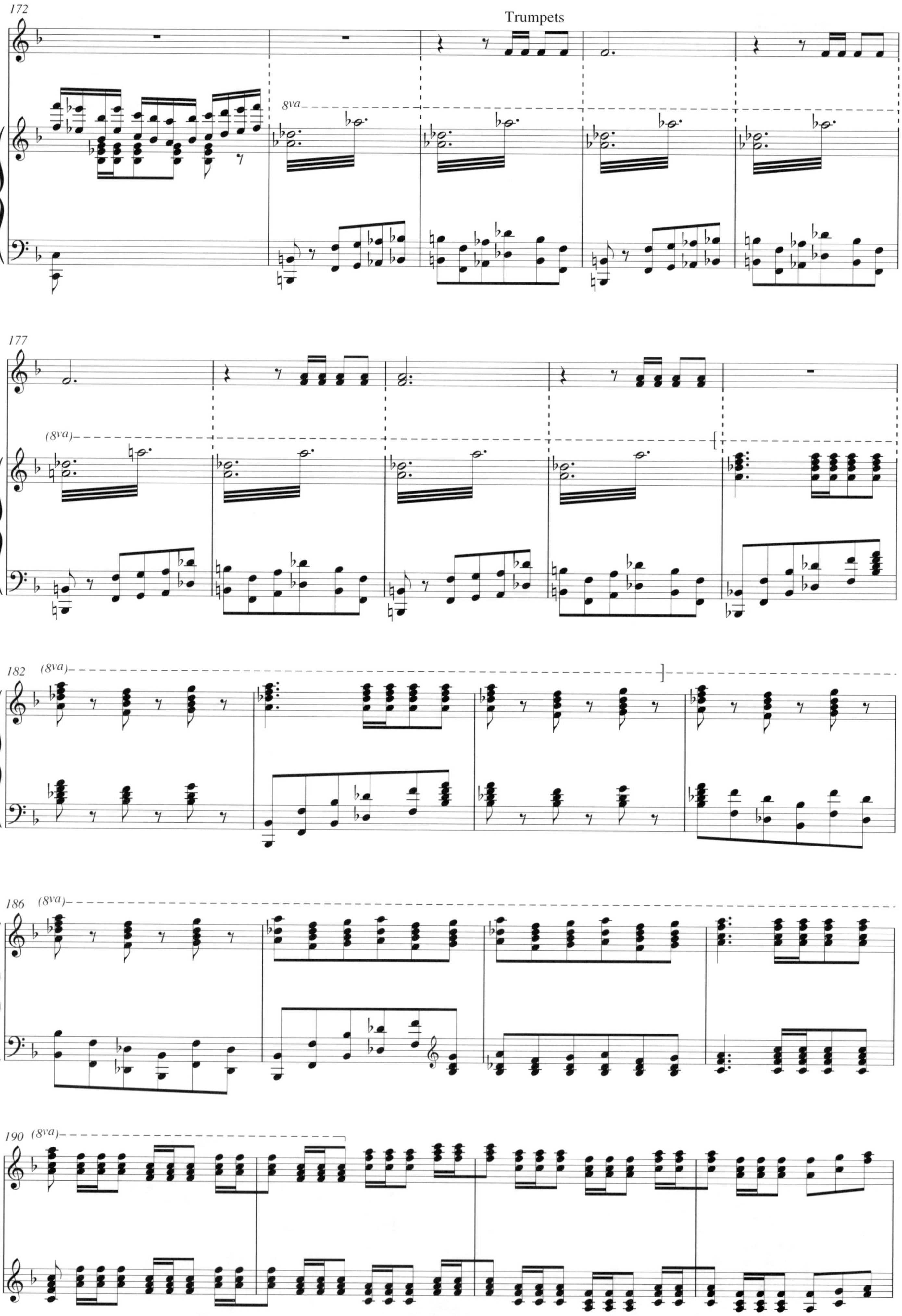
172
Trumpets
8va
177
(8va)
182
(8va)
186
(8va)
190
(8va)

poco a poco accelerando

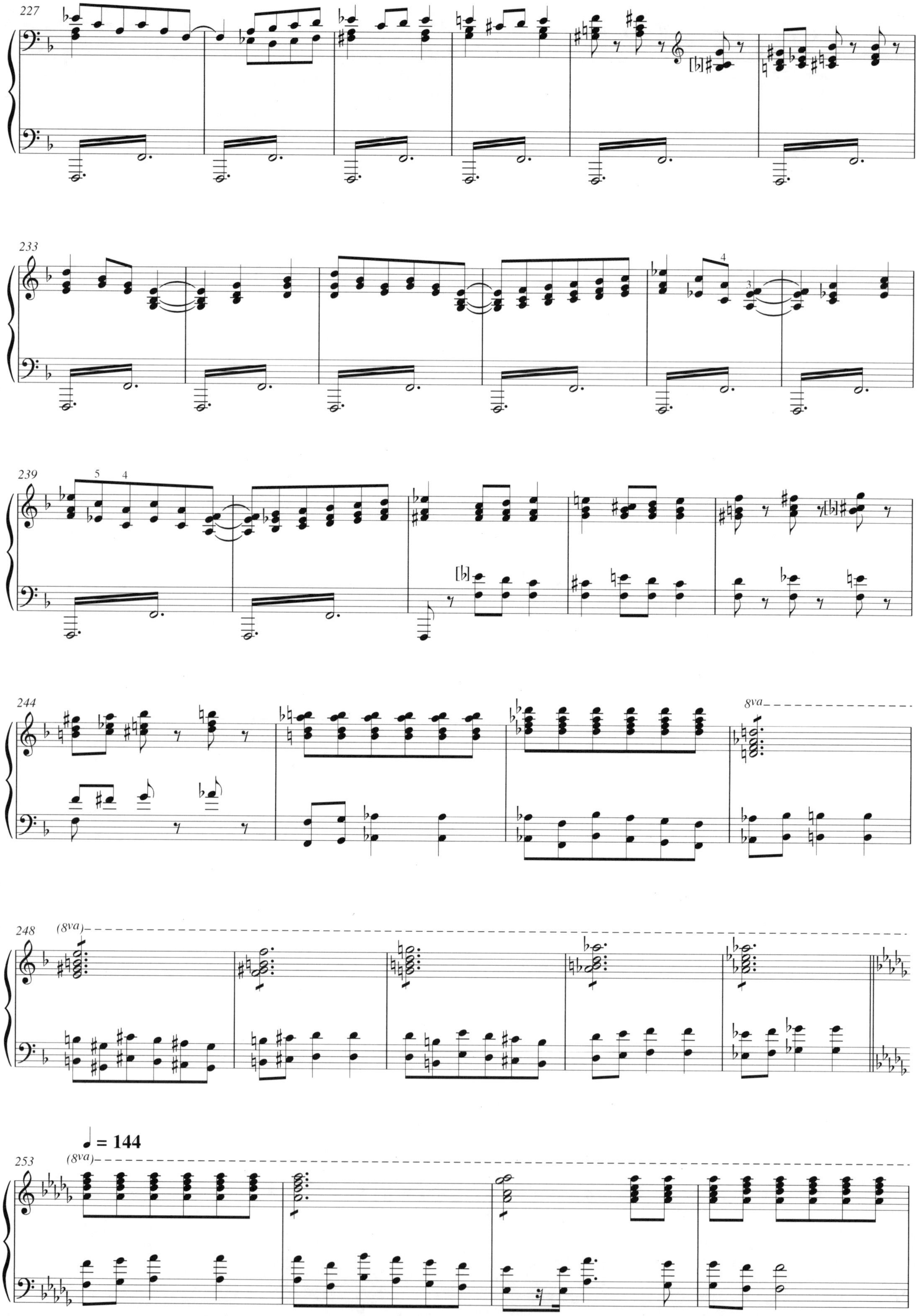
227
233
239
244
8va
248
(8va)
♩ = 144
253
(8va)

67

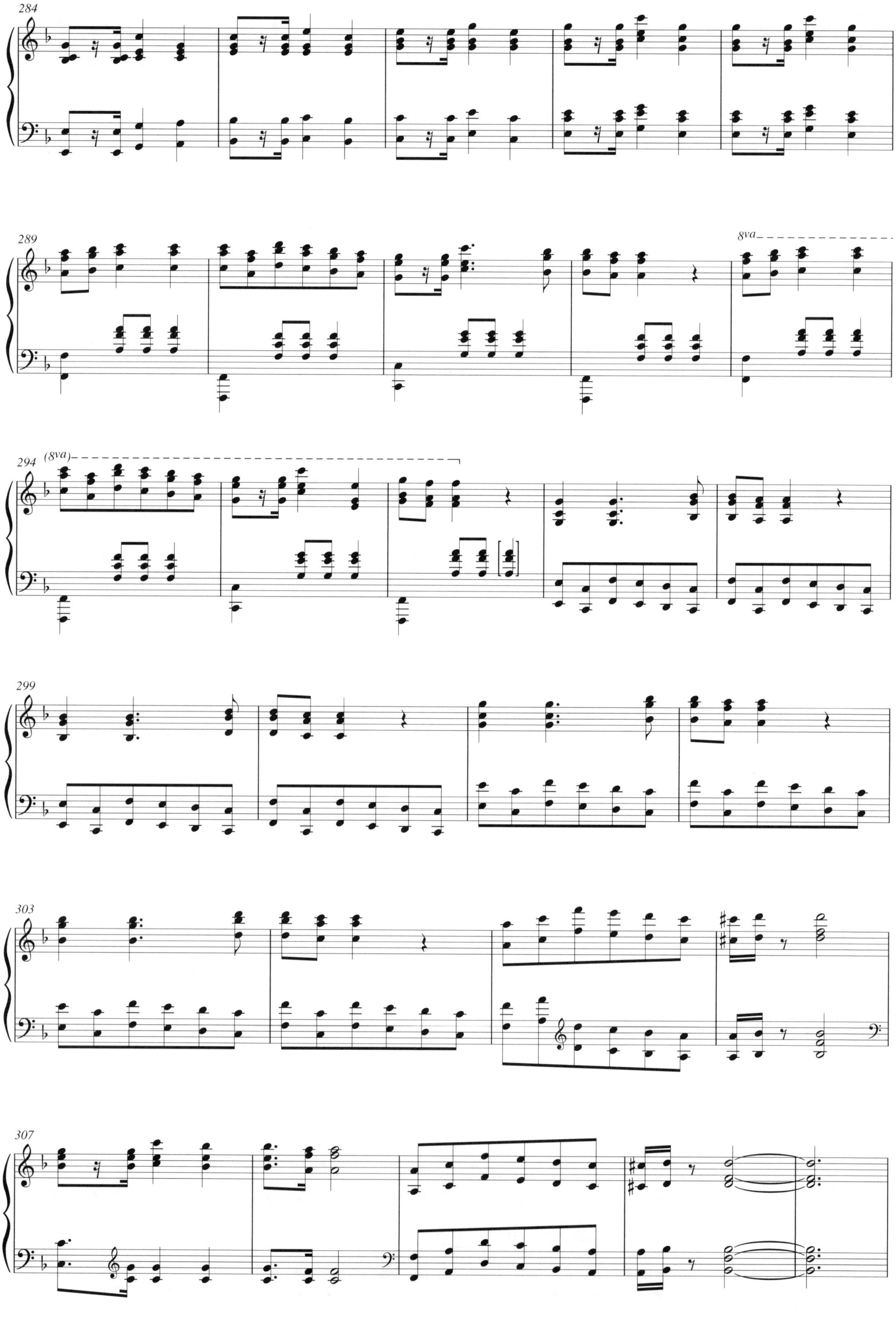
284
289
8va
294
(8va)
299
303
307

69

Scene 4
Orchestral Interlude, "Salve Polonia"
[I]

8
Cl. 1, 2
in A
a 2
f
Bn. 1, 2
a 2
f
Hn. 1, 2
in E
f
Vn. 2
mf
Va.
mf
Vc.
mf
Cb.
mf
15
Ob. 1, 2
dolce
Cl. 1, 2
in A
mp
espressivo
Bn. 1, 2
Vn. 2
Va.
Vc.
Cb.

A
22
Fl. 1, 2
Ob. 1, 2
Cl. 1, 2
in A
Bn. 1, 2
Vn. 2
Va.
Vc.
Cb.
dolce
1
espressivo
espressivo
espressivo
[espressivo]
arco
sostenuto espressivo
[unisoni]
arco
sostenuto espressivo
28
Fl. 1, 2
Ob. 1, 2
Cl. 1, 2
in A
Bn. 1, 2
Vn. 2
Va.
Vc.
Cb.
mf
mf
mf

74

46
Fl. 1, 2
Ob. 1, 2
Cl. 1, 2 in A
Bn. 1, 2
Hn. 1, 2 in E
Vn. 2
pizz.
Va.
pizz.
Vc.
Cb.
53
B
Un poco più lento
dolce
sempre espressivo
Fl. 1, 2
Ob. 1, 2
dolce
Cl. 1, 2 in A
sempre espressivo
Bn. 1, 2
Hn. 1, 2 in E
Un poco più lento
pizz.
Vn. 1
pizz.
Vn. 2
[arco]
Va.
sempre espressivo
pizz.
Vc.
sempre espressivo
pizz.
divisi
[unisoni]
Cb.

59
C
Fl. 1, 2
Cl. 1, 2 in A
Bn. 1, 2
Hn. 1, 2 in E
Vn. 1
Vn. 2
Va.
Vc.
Cb.
1
p
1 cantando
espressivo
pizz.
arco
pizz
65
D
cresc.
p dolce
arco
p
sehr ruhig

71
Fl. 1, 2
Ob. 1, 2
Cl. 1, 2 in A
Bn. 1, 2
Hn. 1, 2 in E
Timp.
Vn. 1
Vn. 2
Va.
Vc.
Cb.
espressivo
p
pp
mp
pizz.
un poco marcato

78

*Die Wiederholung bleibt dem Belieben des Dirigenten überlassen. [Falls sie statt findet, sollen die 23 Takte, dieser Seite *ppp* gespielt werden.]

†[Printed at this point in the piano score is a psalm quotation: "passer invenit sibi domum, et turtur nidum sibi, ubi reponat pullos suos. Altaria tua, Domine virtutum." (Psalm 83:3–4)]

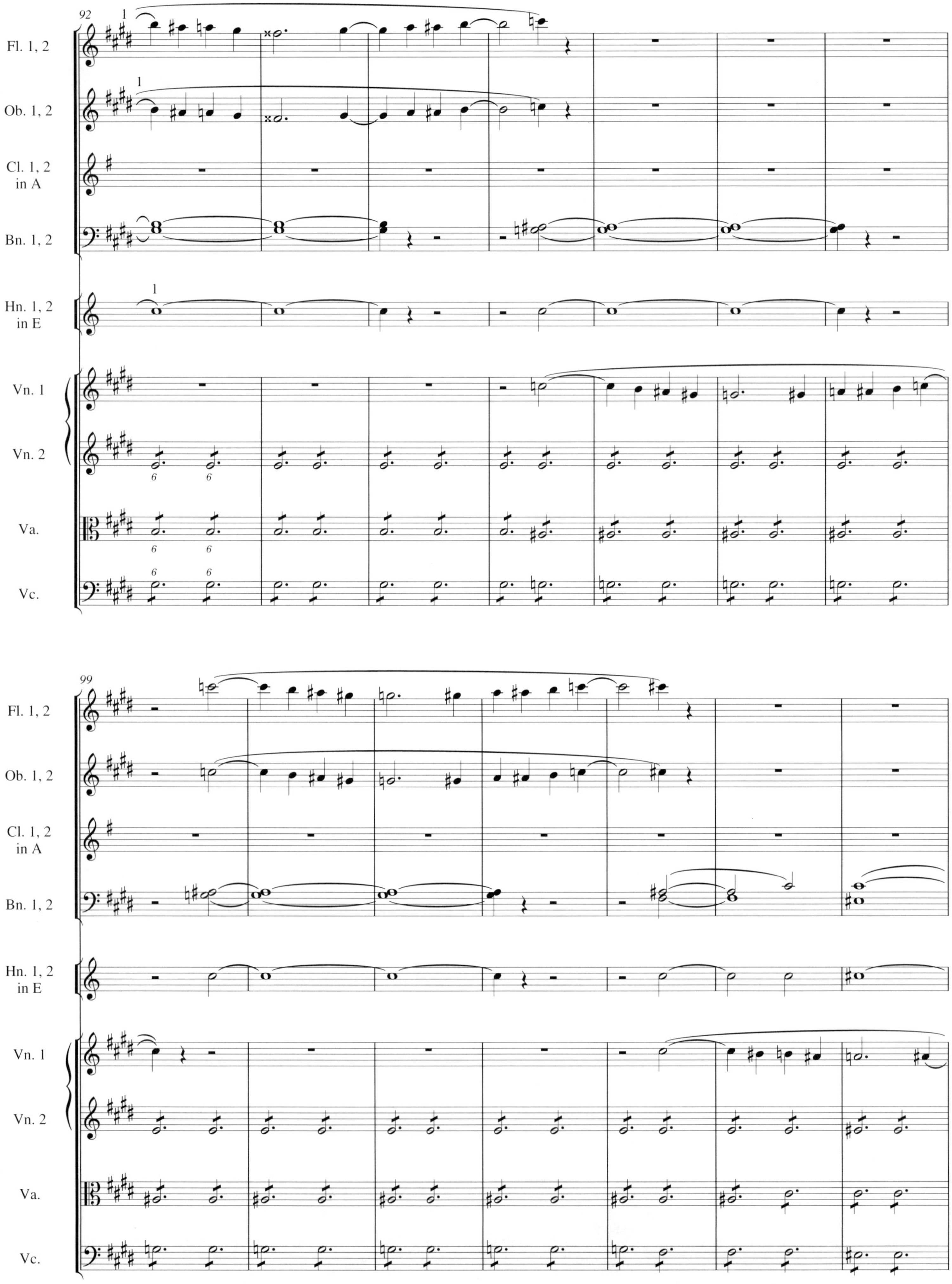
92
1
Fl. 1, 2
Ob. 1, 2
Cl. 1, 2
in A
Bn. 1, 2
Hn. 1, 2
in E
Vn. 1
Vn. 2
Va.
Vc.
99

106
Fl. 1, 2
Ob. 1, 2
Cl. 1, 2
in A
Bn. 1, 2
Hn. 1, 2
in E
Vn. 1
Vn. 2
Va.
Vc.
F
111
Fl. 1, 2
Ob. 1, 2
Cl. 1, 2
in A
Bn. 1, 2
1
a 2
Hn. 1, 2
in E
accentato
divisi
Vn. 1
sempre legato
Vn. 2
Va.
Vc.
Only 2 Basses
[arco]
Cb.
mf espressivo

116
Fl. 1, 2
Ob. 1, 2
Cl. 1, 2
in A
Bn. 1, 2
a 2
Hn. 1, 2
in E
Vn. 1
Vn. 2
Va.
Vc.
Cb.
[All Basses]
mf espressivo

121
Fl. 1, 2
Ob. 1, 2
Cl. 1, 2
in A
Bn. 1, 2
Hn. 1, 2
in E
Hn. 3, 4
in E
solo
dolce
Tpt. 1, 2
in E
espressivo
Tb.
B. Trb.
Tb.
pp
Vn. 1
Vn. 2
Va.
Vc.
Cb.

127
Fl. 1, 2
Ob. 1, 2
Cl. 1, 2 in A
Bn. 1, 2
Hn. 1, 2 in E
Hn. 3, 4 in E
solo
Tpt. 1, 2 in E
Tb.
B. Trb. Tb.
sempre p
Only 2 Violins
Vn. 1
Vn. 2
Va.
Vc.
Cb.

85

86

150
Fl. 1, 2
Ob. 1, 2
Cl. 1, 2 in A
Bn. 1, 2
Hn. 1, 2 in E
Tpt. 1, 2 in E
Vn. 1
Vn. 2
Va.
Vc.
Cb.
più appassionato e cresc.
più appassionato
solo
espressivo
arco
marcato

154
Fl. 1, 2
Ob. 1, 2
Cl. 1, 2 in A
Bn. 1, 2
Hn. 1, 2 in E
Hn. 3, 4 in E
Tpt. 1, 2 in E
B. Trb. Tb.
Timp.
Vn. 1
Vn. 2
Va.
Vc.
Cb.
[a 2]
a 2
rinforzando
[rinforzando]
solo
p
pp
[unisoni]

89

161
Fl. 1, 2
Ob. 1, 2
Cl. 1, 2 in A
[cresc.]
Bn. 1, 2
1
[cresc.]
Hn. 1, 2 in E
[1]
1
Hn. 3, 4 in E
[3]
Tpt. 1, 2 in E
B. Trb. Tb.
Timp.
Vn. 1
[6]
3
cresc.
più rinforzando
Vn. 2
cresc.
[più rinforzando]
Va.
divisi
non divisi
cresc.
Vc.
cresc.
Cb.
pizz.
mf

91

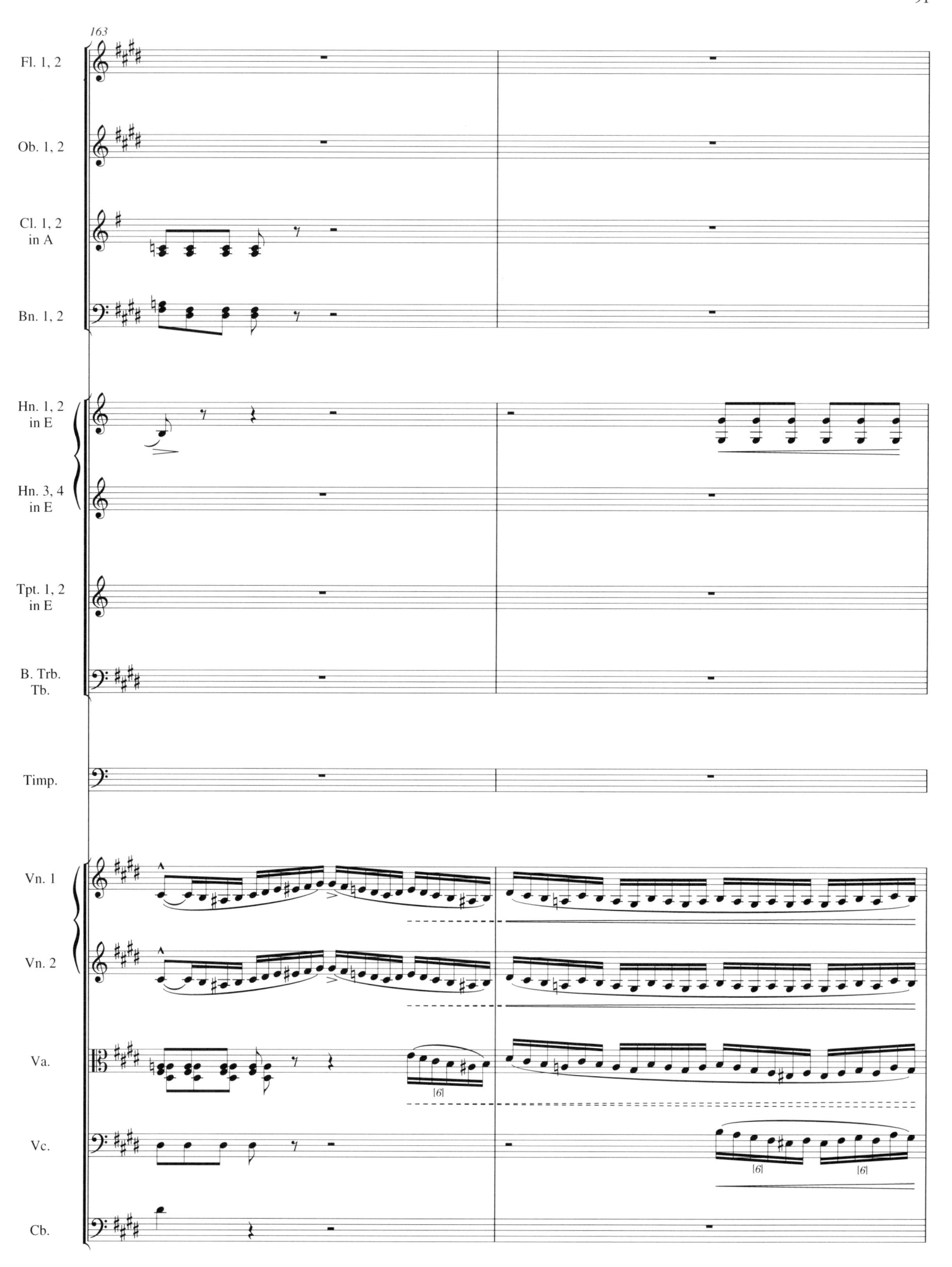

92

93

94

N. B. Wenn nur die erste Hälfte dieses Stückes aufgeführt wird, hier schliessen.

II

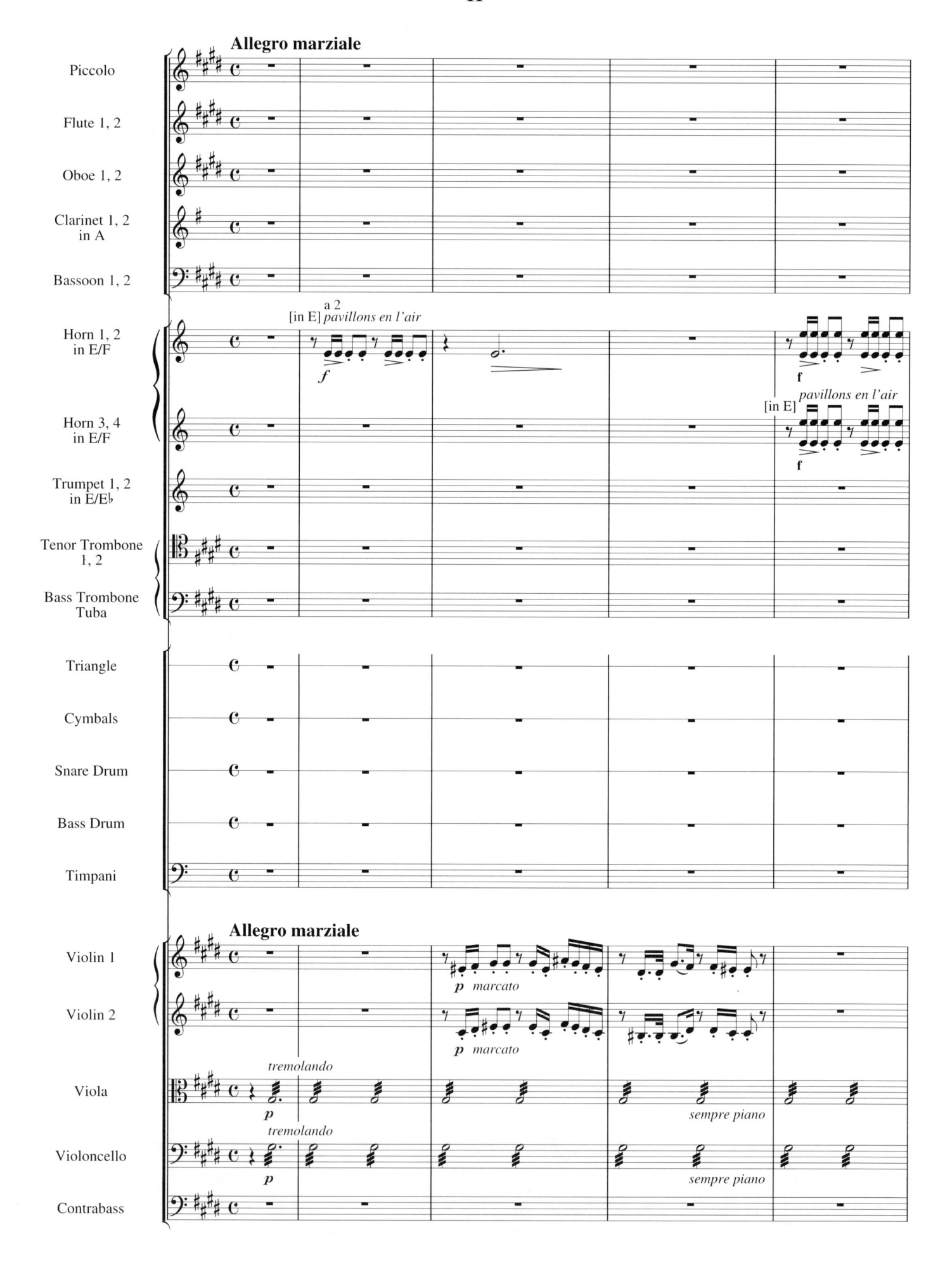

97

11
crescendo
Picc.
Fl. 1, 2
1
a 2
Ob. 1, 2
Cl. 1, 2
in A
Bn. 1, 2
[a 2]
Hn. 1, 2
in E
Hn. 3, 4
in E
Tpt. 1, 2
in E
T. Trb.
1, 2
B. Trb.
Tb.
Sn. Drum
p
crescendo
Vn. 1
Vn. 2
Va.
Vc.
Cb.

In vier Viertel taktieren
(Non troppo presto)
14
Picc.
Fl. 1, 2
Ob. 1, 2
Cl. 1, 2
in A
Bn. 1, 2
a 2
ff
Hn. 1, 2
in E
Hn. 3, 4
in F
Tpt. 1, 2
in E
T. Trb.
1, 2
B. Trb.
Tb.
Trgl.
Cym.
Sn. Drum
B. Drum
Timp.
p
In vier Viertel taktieren
(Non troppo presto)
1
2
3
4
1
2
[unisoni]
Vn. 1
Vn. 2
Va.
Vc.
Cb.
sempre staccato

20
A
Picc.
Fl. 1, 2
Ob. 1, 2
Cl. 1, 2 in A
Bn. 1, 2
a 2
Hn. 1, 2 in E
Hn. 3, 4 in F
Tpt. 1, 2 in E
T. Trb. 1, 2
[a 2]
B. Trb. Tb.
B. Trb.
Cym.
Sn. Drum
Timp.
Vn. 1
Vn. 2
Va.
Vc.
Cb.
sf
fff
f
mf
3
4
1
2
3
4

101

30
Picc.
Fl. 1, 2
Ob. 1, 2
Cl. 1, 2 in A
Bn. 1, 2
[a 2]
in F
pavillons en l'air
Hn. 1, 2 in F
Hn. 3, 4 in F
a 2
Sn. Drum
Vn. 1
Vn. 2
Va.
sempre piano
Vc.
sempre piano
p [marcato]
Cb.
p [marcato]

34
crescendo
Picc.
Fl. 1, 2
1
a 2
Ob. 1, 2
p
Cl. 1, 2
in A
p
Bn. 1, 2
Hn. 1, 2
in F
p
Hn. 3, 4
in F
Sn. Drum
p
p
p
un poco cresc.
crescendo
divisi
Vn. 1
divisi
Vn. 2
Va.
Vc.
Cb.

B
38
In vier Viertel taktieren
Picc.
Fl. 1, 2
Ob. 1, 2
Cl. 1, 2 in A
Bn. 1, 2
a 2
Hn. 1, 2 in F
Hn. 3, 4 in F
Sn. Drum
Timp.
ff
p
In vier Viertel taktieren
1
2
3
4
1
2
[unisoni]
[unisoni]
Vn. 1
Vn. 2
Va.
Vc.
Cb.
sempre staccato

45
Picc.
Fl. 1, 2
Ob. 1, 2
Cl. 1, 2 in A
Bn. 1, 2
Hn. 1, 2 in F
Hn. 3, 4 in F
[a 2]
T. Trb. 1, 2
B. Trb.
B. Trb. Tb.
Cym.
Sn. Drum
Timp.
3
4
[1
2
3
4]
Vn. 1
Vn. 2
Va.
Vc.
Cb.

51
Picc.
Fl. 1, 2
Ob. 1, 2
Cl. 1, 2
in A
Bn. 1, 2
Hn. 1, 2
in F
Hn. 3, 4
in F
Tpt. 1, 2
in E♭
T. Trb.
1, 2
B. Trb.
Tb.
Cym.
Sn. Drum
Vn. 1
Vn. 2
Va.
Vc.
Cb.
a 2
[a 2]
in E♭
1
B. Trb.
Tb.
divisi
ten.
fff
ff
f

107

67
C
Picc.
Fl. 1, 2
Ob. 1, 2
Bn. 1, 2
Hn. 1, 2 in F
Hn. 3, 4 in F
Tpt. 1, 2 in E♭
T. Trb. 1, 2
B. Trb. Tb.
Cym.
Sn. Drum
Timp.
Vn. 1
Vn. 2
Va.
Vc.
Cb.
[a 2]
a 2
8va
ten.
1
ff

75
Picc.
ten.
(8va)
Fl. 1, 2
[a 2]
Ob. 1, 2
Bn. 1, 2
Hn. 1, 2 in F
a 2
Hn. 3, 4 in F
Tpt. 1, 2 in E♭
T. Trb. 1, 2
B. Trb. Tb.
B. Trb.
Cym.
Sn. Drum
Timp.
Vn. 1
Vn. 2
Va.
[non divisi]
[divisi]
Vc.
Cb.

110

91
D
Fl. 1, 2
Ob. 1, 2
Cl. 1, 2
in A
mf
Bn. 1, 2
mf
Hn. 1, 2
in F
Hn. 3, 4
in F
T. Trb.
1, 2
B. Trb.
Tb.
Sn. Drum
Vn. 1
ten.
Vn. 2
ten.
Va.
mf
Vc.
mf
Cb.
mf

99
Picc.
Fl. 1, 2
[a 2]
Ob. 1, 2
ff
Cl. 1, 2 in A
[a 2]
f
Bn. 1, 2
f
Hn. 1, 2 in F
a 2
Hn. 3, 4 in E
T. Trb. 1, 2
B. Trb. Tb.
Trgl.
Sn. Drum
Vn. 1
ten.
Vn. 2
ten.
Va.
ten.
Vc.
ten.
Cb.
ten.

106
E
Picc.
Fl. 1, 2
Ob. 1, 2
Cl. 1, 2
in A
Bn. 1, 2
[a 2]
Hn. 1, 2
in F
Hn. 3, 4
in E
in E
T. Trb.
1, 2
staccato
B. Trb.
Tb.
staccato
Trgl.
Sn. Drum
Vn. 1
pizz.
Vn. 2
[divisi]
[unisoni]
pizz.
Va.
divisi
[unisoni]
pizz.
Vc.
pizz.
Cb.

112
Picc.
Fl. 1, 2
Ob. 1, 2
Cl. 1, 2
in A
Bn. 1, 2
Hn. 1, 2
in F
Hn. 3, 4
in E
T. Trb.
1, 2
B. Trb.
Tb.
Trgl.
Sn. Drum
Vn. 1
Vn. 2
Va.
Vc.
Cb.
arco
ff
f

118
Picc.
Fl. 1, 2
Ob. 1, 2
Cl. 1, 2
in A
Bn. 1, 2
Hn. 1, 2
in F
Hn. 3, 4
in E
Tpt. 1, 2
in E♭
T. Trb.
1, 2
B. Trb.
Tb.
Trgl.
Sn. Drum
Timp.
Vn. 1
Vn. 2
Va.
Vc.
Cb.
a 2
ff
mp
mf
f
pizz.
arco
ten.

116

131
F
Picc.
ff
8va
Fl. 1, 2
ff
Ob. 1, 2
ff
Cl. 1, 2
in A
ff
a 2
Bn. 1, 2
ff
a 2
Hn. 1, 2
in F
ff
[a 2]
Hn. 3, 4
in E
ff
T. Trb.
1, 2
B. Trb.
B. Trb.
Tb.
Vn. 1
ff
ten.
ten.
ten.
Vn. 2
ff
ten.
ten.
ten.
Va.
ff
ten.
ten.
ten.
Vc.
ff
ten.
ten.
ten.
Cb.
ff
ten.
ten.
ten.

138
Picc.
(8va)
a 2
Fl. 1, 2
Ob. 1, 2
Cl. 1, 2
in A
a 2
Bn. 1, 2
Hn. 1, 2
in F
[a 2]
Hn. 3, 4
in E
T. Trb.
1, 2
B. Trb.
B. Trb.
Tb.
ten.
Vn. 1
ff impetuoso
ten.
Vn. 2
ff marcatissimo
ten.
Va.
ff marcatissimo
ten.
Vc.
ff marcatissimo
ten.
Cb.
ff [marcatissimo]

119

152
Fl. 1, 2
Ob. 1, 2
1
Bn. 1, 2
1
Hn. 1, 2 in F
Hn. 3, 4 in E
[non troppo f]
T. Trb. 1, 2
[dim.]
B. Trb. Tb.
B. Trb.
[dim.]
Sn. Drum
pp
pp
Timp.
p
p
Vn. 1
Vn. 2
Va.
Vc.
Cb.

159
Fl. 1, 2
Ob. 1, 2
Cl. 1, 2 in A
Bn. 1, 2
Hn. 3, 4 in E
T. Trb. 1, 2
B. Trb. Tb.
Sn. Drum
B. Drum
Timp.
Vn. 1
Vn. 2
Va.
Vc.
Cb.
dolente
dim.

166
Picc.
[dolente]
Fl. 1, 2
f
Ob. 1, 2
f
Cl. 1, 2
in A
f
Bn. 1, 2
f
Hn. 1, 2
in F
[dolente]
T. Trb.
1, 2
f
p
B. Trb.
B. Trb.
Tb.
f
p
Sn. Drum
f
pp
B. Drum
p
f
p
Vn. 1
ff violente
Vn. 2
ff violente
p
Va.
ff violente
p
Vc.
ff violente
p
Cb.
ff violente
p

123

180
un poco rit.
Picc.
Fl. 1, 2
Ob. 1, 2
Cl. 1, 2 in A
Bn. 1, 2
T. Trb. 1, 2
1
p
B. Trb. Tb.
B. Trb.
p
Timp.
p
p
pp
un poco rit.
Vn. 1
pp
pp
Vn. 2
pp
pp
Va.
pp
pp
Vc.
pp
pp
Cb.
pp
pp

125

193
Fl. 1, 2
p staccato
cresc. [
Ob. 1, 2
[staccato]
[cresc.
Cl. 1, 2
in A
cresc. [
Bn. 1, 2
cresc. [
Hn. 1, 2
in E
1
a 2
cresc.
Hn. 3, 4
in E
3
Sn. Drum
p
Timp.
crescendo poco a poco
Vn. 1
cresc.
Vn. 2
cresc.
Va.
divisi
cresc.
Vc.
cresc.
Cb.
cresc.

127

128

211
sempre un poco accelerando il Tempo
Picc.
Fl. 1, 2
8va
Ob. 1, 2
Cl. 1, 2
in A
Bn. 1, 2
Hn. 1, 2
in E
a 2
Hn. 3, 4
in E
T. Trb.
1, 2
B. Trb.
Tb.
B. Trb.
B. Drum
Timp.
sempre un poco accelerando il Tempo
Vn. 1
Vn. 2
Va.
Vc.
Cb.
p
mp
pp

216
Picc.
Fl. 1, 2
8va
a 2
Ob. 1, 2
cresc.
Cl. 1, 2 in A
Bn. 1, 2
Hn. 1, 2 in E
Hn. 3, 4 in E
Tpt. 1, 2 in E
1
T. Trb. 1, 2
B. Trb. Tb.
B. Trb.
B. Drum
Timp.
Vn. 1
Vn. 2
Va.
Vc.
Cb.

131

226
Picc.
Fl. 1, 2
8va
a 2
Ob. 1, 2
[più cresc.]
Cl. 1, 2
in A
[più cresc.]
Bn. 1, 2
a 2
[più cresc.]
Hn. 1, 2
in E
[più] cresc.
Hn. 3, 4
in E
[più] cresc.
Tpt. 1, 2
in E
cresc.
T. Trb.
1, 2
p
cresc.
B. Trb.
Tb.
p
B. Trb.
cresc.
Sn. Drum
un poco cresc.
B. Drum
p
un poco cresc.
Timp.
p
[un poco cresc.]
Vn. 1
più cresc.
Vn. 2
più cresc.
Va.
più cresc.
Vc.
più cresc.
non divisi
Cb.

133

236
J
Picc.
Fl. 1, 2
a 2
(8va)
Ob. 1, 2
Cl. 1, 2
in A
8va
Bn. 1, 2
Hn. 1, 2
in E
Hn. 3, 4
in E
Tpt. 1, 2
in E
T. Trb.
1, 2
B. Trb.
Tb.
Trgl.
Cym.
Sn. Drum
B. Drum
Timp.
Vn. 1
Vn. 2
Va.
Vc.
Cb.
fff
ff
sf
f
ff marc[atissimo]
fff staccato

241
Picc.
(8va)
Fl. 1, 2
Ob. 1, 2
(8va)
Cl. 1, 2
in A
Bn. 1, 2
Hn. 1, 2
in E
Hn. 3, 4
in E
Tpt. 1, 2
in E
T. Trb.
1, 2
B. Trb.
Tb.
Trgl.
Cym.
Sn. Drum
ff
B. Drum
Timp.
Vn. 1
Vn. 2
Va.
Vc.
Cb.

136

137

258
lunga
Picc.
a 2
Fl. 1, 2
Ob. 1, 2
Cl. 1, 2
in A
a 2
Bn. 1, 2
Hn. 1, 2
in E
Hn. 3, 4
in E
Tpt. 1, 2
in E
T. Trb.
1, 2
B. Trb.
Tb.
Trgl.
Cym.
Sn. Drum
B. Drum
Timp.
lunga
Vn. 1
Vn. 2
Va.
Vc.
Cb.

264
K
In vier Viertel taktieren
Fl. 1, 2
Ob. 1, 2
Cl. 1, 2
in A
Bn. 1, 2
Hn. 1, 2
in E
Timp.
Cb.
dolce
In vier Viertel taktieren
4 1 2 3 4 1 2 3 4
pizz.
273
Va.
Vc.
pizz.
arco

281
Picc.
Fl. 1, 2
Ob. 1, 2
Cl. 1, 2 in A
Bn. 1, 2
Hn. 1, 2 in E
Hn. 3, 4 in E
Tpt. 1, 2 in E
T. Trb. 1, 2
B. Trb. Tb.
Cym.
B. Drum
Timp.
Vn. 1
Vn. 2
Va.
Vc.
Cb.
[a 2]
cresc.
B. Trb.
[cresc.
[cresc.]
arco
pp
p
f

287
lunga
L
Picc.
Fl. 1, 2
Ob. 1, 2
p dolce
Cl. 1, 2 in A
p dolce
Bn. 1, 2
p
Hn. 1, 2 in E
p
Hn. 3, 4 in E
Tpt. 1, 2 in E
T. Trb. 1, 2
B. Trb. Tb.
Cym.
B. Drum
Timp.
p
p
lunga
4
1
2
3
4
Vn. 1
Vn. 2
Va.
Vc.
Cb.
pizz.
p

142

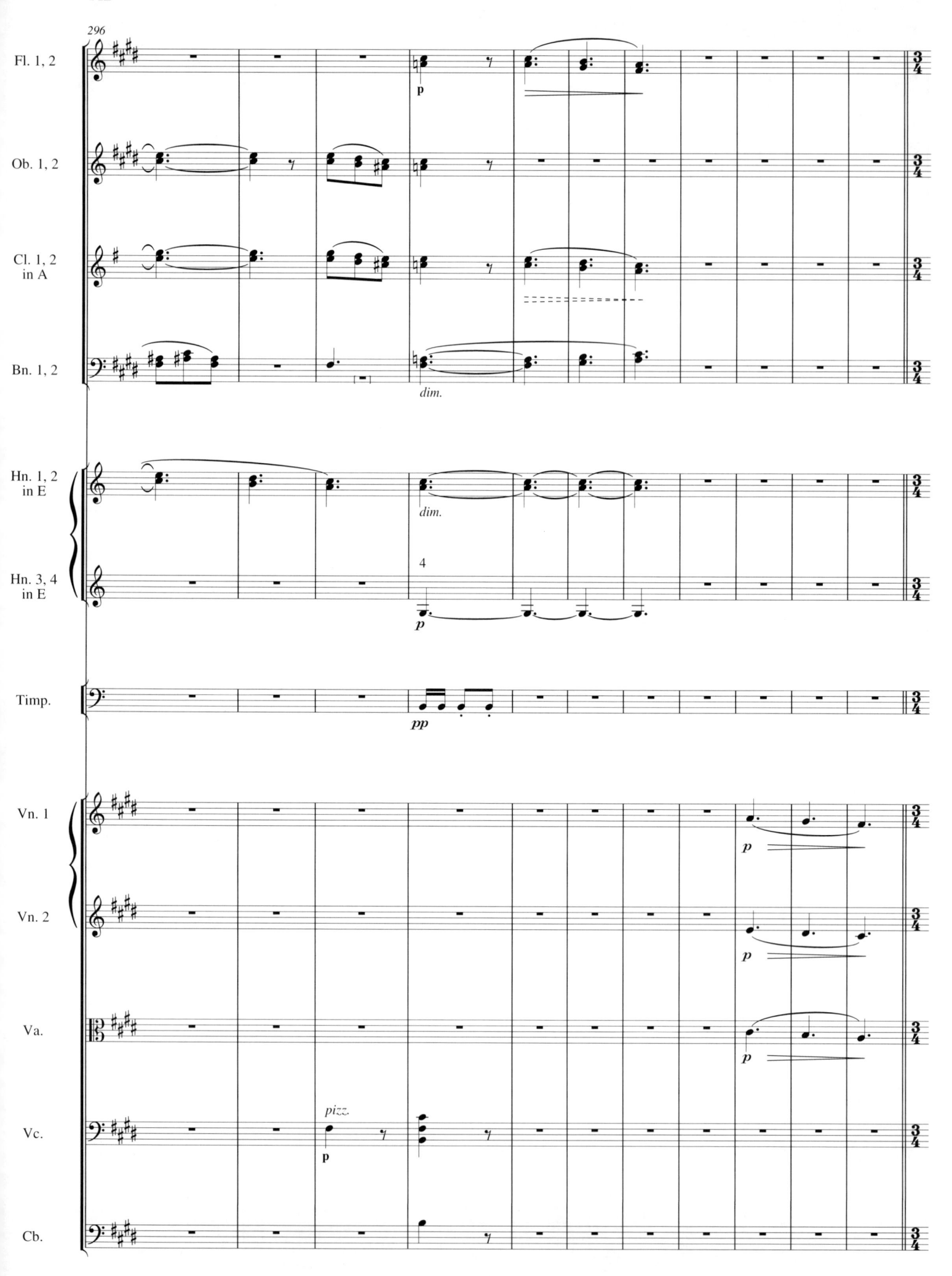

143

319
Fl. 1, 2
Ob. 1, 2
Cl. 1, 2 in A
Bn. 1, 2
Hn. 1, 2 in E
Hn. 3, 4 in E
Tpt. 1, 2 in E
T. Trb. 1, 2
B. Trb. Tb.
Timp.
Vn. 1
Vn. 2
Va.
Vc.
Cb.
a 2
[a 2]
ten.
[ten.]
B. Trb.
f
ff
mf

325
N
[Animato]
Picc.
Fl. 1, 2
Ob. 1, 2
Cl. 1, 2 in A
Bn. 1, 2
Hn. 1, 2 in E
Hn. 3, 4 in E
Tpt. 1, 2 in E
T. Trb. 1, 2
B. Trb. Tb.
Cym.
Sn. Drum
Timp.
Vn. 1
Vn. 2
Va.
Vc.
Cb.
sempre ff
[a 2]
a 2
8va
ten.
divisi
f
[Animato]

146

147

148

O
350
(tr)
(8va)
[a 2]
a 2
[unisoni]
[divisi]
ten.
ff staccato
ff
f
Picc.
Fl. 1, 2
Ob. 1, 2
Cl. 1, 2 in A
Bn. 1, 2
Hn. 1, 2 in E
Hn. 3, 4 in E
Tpt. 1, 2 in E
T. Trb. 1, 2
B. Trb. Tb.
Trgl.
Cym.
Timp.
Vn. 1
Vn. 2
Va.
Vc.
Cb.

150

365
Fl. 1, 2
[a 2]
ff
Ob. 1, 2
ff
[a 2]
tr
Cl. 1, 2
in A
a 2
Bn. 1, 2
Hn. 1, 2
in E
a 2
f
Hn. 3, 4
in E
f
Vn. 1
Vn. 2
divisi
[unisoni]
Va.
Vc.
Cb.

372
Fl. 1, 2
[a 2]
(tr)
Ob. 1, 2
Cl. 1, 2 in A
Bn. 1, 2
a 2
Hn. 1, 2 in E
a 2
Hn. 3, 4 in E
Vn. 1
Vn. 2
Va.
Vc.
Cb.

378
Picc.
Fl. 1, 2
a 2
Ob. 1, 2
Cl. 1, 2 in A
Bn. 1, 2
Hn. 1, 2 in E
Hn. 3, 4 in E
Tpt. 1, 2 in E
T. Trb. 1, 2
B. Trb. Tb.
Cym.
Timp.
divisi
Vn. 1
divisi
Vn. 2
Va.
[divisi]
[unisoni]
Vc.
Cb.

385
Picc.
Fl. 1, 2
Ob. 1, 2
Cl. 1, 2 in A
Bn. 1, 2
Hn. 1, 2 in E
Hn. 3, 4 in E
Tpt. 1, 2 in E
T. Trb. 1, 2
B. Trb. Tb.
Trgl.
Cym.
Sn. Drum
Timp.
Vn. 1
Vn. 2
Va.
Vc.
Cb.
a 2
[a 2]
ff
[unisoni]

393
Ob. 1, 2
Cl. 1, 2
in A
Bn. 1, 2
Hn. 1, 2
in E
Hn. 3, 4
in E
Tpt. 1, 2
in E
T. Trb.
1, 2
B. Trb.
Tb.
a 2
Trgl.
Cym.
Sn. Drum
Timp.
Vn. 1
Vn. 2
Va.
Vc.
Cb.

Psalm 129, "De profundis"

157

158

159

T: De pro- fun- dis cla- ma- vi ad te, Do- mi- ne,

B: De pro- fun- dis cla- ma- vi ad te, Do- - mi- ne,

T: Do- mi- ne ex- au- di vo- cem me- - am!

B: Do- mi- ne ex- au- di vo- cem me- - am!

Bar. De pro- fun- dis cla- ma- vi ad te, Do- mi- ne, Do- - mi- ne ex- au- - - di vo- cem me- am,

119
Do- - mi- ne ex- au- di vo- cem me- am! Fi- ant
p dolce
125
au- res tu- ae in- ter- den- tes in vo- cem de- pre- ca- ti- o- nis
131
me- ae.
dolcissimo
dim.
138
mf
Si i- ni- qui- ta- tes ob- ser- va- ve- ris
145
ritenuto
Do- - mi- ne, quis su- sti- ne- bit? Quis su- sti-

161

177
Do- mi- ne. Su- sti- nu- it a- ni- ma me- a
183
in ver- - bo e- jus spe- ra- vit a- ni- ma
p
189
me- a, a- ni- ma me- a spe- ra- - vit.
p
196
dim.
204
p
A cu- sto- di- a ma- tu- ti- na u- - sque ad no- ctem

163

232
Bar.
et i- - pse re- di- met
Org.
sempre p
239
I- - sra- el ex o- mni- bus i- ni- qui-
245
-ta- ti- bus e- jus,
p
251
Bar.
et i- - pse re- di- met I-
2 Tenor Soloists
T
Et i- - pse re- di- met I-
2 Bass Soloists
B
Et i- - pse re- di- met I-
Org.
p

-sra- el ___ ex o- mni- bus i- ni- qui- ta- ti- bus

e- jus.

Solo
e- jus, ex o- mni-bus i- ni- qui- ta- ti- bus ___ e- jus.

Bar.

Org.

I- -pse, i- -pse

re- di- met,

et i- pse re- di-

-met.

pp

sempre diminuendo

pp ritenuto

Chorus, "Salve Polonia"

7
Hn. 1, 2 in E
Hn. 3, 4 in E
Timp.
p un poco marcato
[sempre staccato]
S
Sal- ve,
A
Sal- ve,
T
p [dolce]
Sal- - ve Po- lo- - ni- a!
Vn. 2
Va.
Vc.
pizz.
arco
Cb.
un poco marcato
12
Bn. 1, 2
p
Hn. 1, 2 in E
Hn. 3, 4 in E
Timp.
S
sal- ve Po- lo- - ni- a!
A
sal- ve Po- lo- - ni- a!
T
Sal- - ve Po- lo-
Vn. 2
Va.
Vc.
pizz.
Cb.

18
Fl. 1, 2
a 2
p
Ob. 1, 2
a 2
p
Cl. 1, 2 in A
p
Bn. 1, 2
a 2
espressivo (Hn. 1)
Hn. 1, 2 in E
Hn. 3, 4 in E
Timp.
Bar.
p
Sal- -
S
Sal- ve, sal- ve, sal- - ve Po- lo- ni-
A
Sal- ve, sal- ve, sal- - ve Po- lo- ni-
T
- ni- a! Sal- ve, sal- ve, sal- - ve Po- lo- ni-
B
p
Sal- - ve Po- lo- ni-
Vn. 1
p
Vn. 2
Va.
Vc.
Cb.
arco
marcato ed espressivo

170

171

172

173

174

54
Bar.
-a!
8va
Vn. 1
Vn. 2
Va.
Vc.
Cb.
f [staccato]
f [staccato]
f [staccato]
59
a 2
Fl. 1, 2
Ob. 1, 2
Cl. 1, 2 in A
[a 2]
Timp.
S
Sal- ve, sal- ve Po- lo- - ni- a!
A
Sal- ve, sal- ve Po- lo- - ni- a!
T
Sal- - ve, sal- ve Po- lo- - ni- a! Sal-
(8va)
pizz.

64
Fl. 1, 2
a 2
Ob. 1, 2
a 2
Cl. 1, 2 in A
[a 2]
Timp.
S
Sal- ve Po- lo- ni- a! Sal- ve, sal- ve Po- lo-
A
Sal- ve Po- lo- ni- a! Sal- ve, sal- ve Po- lo-
T
- ve Po- lo- - ni- a! Sal- - ve, sal- ve Po- lo-
B
p
Sal- - - ve,
Vn. 1
Vn. 2
divisi
non divisi
Va.
Vc.
Cb.
[arco]

177

178

179

180

181

98
Fl. 1, 2
Ob. 1, 2
Cl. 1, 2 in A
Bn. 1, 2
Hn. 1, 2 in E
Hn. 3, 4 in E
Tpt. 1, 2 in E
Timp.
Bar.
-a! Sal- ve Po- lo- ni-
T
-a!
B
Sal- - ve Po- lo- ni-
Vn. 1
Vn. 2
Va.
Vc.
Cb.
a 2
8va

103
(8va)
Fl. 1, 2
Ob. 1, 2
Cl. 1, 2 in A
2
Bn. 1, 2
Hn. 1, 2 in E
Hn. 3, 4 in E
Tpt. 1, 2 in E
Timp.
Bar.
-a! Sal- ve Po- lo- ni- a,
B
-a! Sal- - ve Po- lo- ni- a!
8va
Vn. 1
Vn. 2
Va.
Vc.
Cb.

Poco a poco animato
108
Bar.
Po- lo- ni- a!
Poco a poco animato
Vn. 1
Vn. 2
f [staccato]
Va.
f [staccato]
Vc.
f [staccato]
Cb.
f [staccato]
115
Volles Werk
Org.
Bar.
Sal- - ve, sal- ve Po- lo- ni- a!
S
Sal- - ve, sal- ve Po- lo- ni-
A
Sal- - ve, sal- ve Po- lo- ni-
T
Sal- - ve, sal- ve Po- lo- ni-
B
Sal- - ve, sal- ve Po- lo- ni-

185

129
Fl. 1, 2
Ob. 1, 2
Cl. 1, 2 in A
Bn. 1, 2
Hn. 1, 2 in E
Hn. 3, 4 in E
Tpt. 1, 2 in E
T. Trb. 1, 2
B. Trb. Tb.
Timp.
Org.
S
A
T
B
Vn. 1
Vn. 2
Va.
Vc.
Cb.
a 2
ff
-ve Po- lo- ni- a! Sal- ve Po- lo-

187

141
a 2
Fl. 1, 2
Ob. 1, 2
Cl. 1, 2
in A
Bn. 1, 2
Hn. 1, 2
in E
Hn. 3, 4
in E
Tpt. 1, 2
in E
T. Trb.
1, 2
B. Trb.
Tb.
Timp.
Bar.
-lo- ni- a, Po- lo-
S
A
T
B
Vn. 1
Vn. 2
Va.
Vc.
Cb.

147
Fl. 1, 2
Ob. 1, 2
Cl. 1, 2 in A
Bn. 1, 2
Hn. 1, 2 in E
Hn. 3, 4 in E
Tpt. 1, 2 in E
T. Trb. 1, 2
B. Trb. Tb.
Timp.
Org.
Bar.
S
A
T
B
Vn. 1
Vn. 2
Va.
Vc.
Cb.
a 2
3
- ni- a, Po- lo- ni- a,

190

158
Fl. 1, 2
Ob. 1, 2
Cl. 1, 2 in A
Bn. 1, 2
Hn. 1, 2 in E
Hn. 3, 4 in E
Tpt. 1, 2 in E
T. Trb. 1, 2
B. Trb. Tb.
Timp.
Org.
Bar.
S
A
T
B
Vn. 1
Vn. 2
Va.
Vc.
Cb.
a 2

163
Fl. 1, 2
Ob. 1, 2
a 2
Cl. 1, 2 in A
a 2
Bn. 1, 2
Hn. 1, 2 in E
Hn. 3, 4 in E
Tpt. 1, 2 in E
a 2
T. Trb. 1, 2
a 2
B. Trb. Tb.
Timp.
Org.
Bar.
S
A
T
B
Vn. 1
Vn. 2
Va.
Vc.
Cb.

Critical Report

Sources

In the following list, "autograph" is understood to mean any manuscript primarily in Liszt's hand, including both drafts and clean copies. Items designated "copy" are primarily in someone else's hand, although in almost every case Liszt annotated or altered the copy. A "printer's manuscript" is a copy submitted by Liszt to his publisher Kahnt for the engraver's use. Square brackets enclose early, "pre-Stanislaus," versions of the interlude and the psalm. The abbreviation GSA is used for the Goethe- und Schiller-Archiv, Weimar.

Manuscripts

Scene 1

Washington, Library of Congress, Rosenthal Collection. Autograph sketches.

Weimar, GSA 60/B3d. Autograph of introduction, the chorus "Qual und Leid," some recitative, and the chorus "Beschütz uns." Orchestral score.

Weimar, GSA 60/B3e. Autograph of introduction, the chorus "Qual und Leid," some recitative, and the chorus "Beschütz uns." Piano score.

Weimar, GSA 60/B3f. Autograph of the aria "Mein Sohn, o still des Volkes Not." Piano score.

Weimar, GSA 60/B3f1. Autograph fragment of chorus "Weh uns!" (1880 variant of opening chorus). Piano score.

Two Polonaises

Weimar, GSA 60/B3h1–2. Autograph, piano two hands.

Orchestral Interlude, "Salve Polonia"

Budapest, Liszt Ferenc Emlékmúzeum, Ms. mus. L. 12. Autograph fragment, piano four hands.

Budapest, Liszt Ferenc Emlékmúzeum, Ms. mus. L. 13. Autograph fragment, piano two hands.

Budapest, Országos Széchényi Könyvtár, Ms. mus. 6.533. Autograph fragment, piano four hands.

[Paris, Bibliothèque Nationale, Ms. 153. Autograph of 1863 version, orchestral score.]

Washington, Library of Congress, ML96.L58. Autograph fragment, orchestral score.

[Weimar, GSA 60/B3g. Autograph of 1863 version, piano four hands.]

[Weimar, GSA 60/B3g1. Copy of 1863 version, piano four hands.]

Weimar, GSA 60/B3n. Photographic reproduction of autograph fragment, piano four hands.

[Weimar, GSA 60/U66. Autograph fragment of 1863 version, piano two hands.]

Weimar, GSA Depositum Hoffmann 5a. Printer's manuscript, orchestral score.

Weimar, GSA Depositum Hoffmann 5b. Proofs, orchestral score.

Weimar, GSA Depositum Hoffmann 5e. Autograph fragment, piano two hands.

Psalm 129, "De profundis"

[Budapest, Országos Széchényi Könyvtár, Ms. mus. 4.809. Autograph of 1880 version for bass or alto.]

Budapest, Országos Széchényi Könyvtár, Ms. mus. 5.632. Autograph fragment of rejected variant.

Budapest, Országos Széchényi Könyvtár, Ms. mus. 6.056. Autograph. A printed copy of the 1880 version—see printed editions below—with additions and corrections in Liszt's hand.

[Washington, Library of Congress, ML96.L58. Autograph fragment of 1880 version for bass or alto.]

[Washington, Library of Congress, Rosenthal Collection. Copy of 1880 version for bass or alto.]

Weimar, GSA 60/B3k. Autograph sketch for a transition between the interlude and the psalm.

Weimar, GSA 60/B3s. Fragmentary copy.

[Weimar, GSA 60/R2a–b. Copies of 1880 version for bass or alto.]

Weimar, GSA Depositum Hoffmann 15a. Printer's manuscript.

[Weimar, GSA Depositum Hoffmann 15b–c. Printer's manuscripts of the 1880 version for bass or alto.]

[Weimar, GSA Depositum Hoffmann 15d. Proofs for the 1880 version for bass.]

Chorus, "Salve Polonia"

Weimar, GSA 60/B3o. Autograph, first version (1882), piano score.

Weimar, GSA 60/B3p. Autograph, second version (1884), piano score.

Weimar, GSA 60/B3q. Autograph draft of final version (1885–86?), piano score.

Weimar, GSA 60/B3r. Autograph fragments of final version, orchestral and piano scores.

Weimar, GSA Depositum Hoffmann 5c. Printer's manuscript, orchestral score.

Weimar, GSA Depositum Hoffmann 5d. Printer's manuscript, piano score.

Printed Editions

[PSALM 129. / "DE PROFUNDIS CLAMAVI" / "AUS DER TIEFE RUFE ICH" / FÜR / EINE BASS- ODER ALTSTIMME / UND / Pianoforte- oder Orgelbegleitung / COMPONIRT VON / FRANZ LISZT / . . . / LEIPZIG, C. F. KAHNT. Version for bass: plate number 2592. Version for alto: plate number 2593.]

Salve Polonia / Interludium / aus dem Oratorium / Stanislaus / componirt von / Franz Liszt / . . . / Leipzig, C. F. Kahnt. Orchestral score: plate number 2764. Piano two hands: plate number 2766. Piano four hands: plate number 2783.

Ausgabe C. F. Kahnt Nachfolger. / Musikbeilage / der / Neuen Zeitschrift / für Musik. / Franz Liszt / Der 129. Psalm / für / Baryton-Solo, Männerchor und Orgel. Plate number 2764.

The editor has used Liszt's autograph (GSA 60/B3d) as the principal source for the first several numbers of scene 1. It consists of three folded sheets paginated 1–12. Each page carries 32 staves and measures 26.9 cm in width and 35 cm in length. The title reads: S<u>t</u> Stanislas. The date reads: 6 Janvier 75 / Villa d'Este / FL. The editor has followed Liszt's directive, given on page 11 of the manuscript, to reproduce the vocal parts of the chorus "Beschütz uns" as they appear in the autograph of the piano score (GSA 60/B3e).

No full score survives for the last number of scene 1, so Liszt's autograph piano score (GSA 60/B3f) serves as the principal source here. It consists of four leaves paginated a–g (no letter assigned to 4v). Each page carries 14 staves and measures 27 cm in width and 34.6 to 34.9 cm in length. No title or date is given. The last page of the manuscript is a crossed-out copy, in Liszt's hand, of the hymn "Gaude Mater Polonia."

The principal source for the polonaises is Liszt's autograph manuscript (GSA 60/B3h1–2): twenty-five pages in upright format, numbered 1–7, 1–18, plus one small leaf. There are 10 staves per page. The title reads: Deux Polonaises / (de l'oratorio "St. Stanislas"). A facsimile of the first page can be found in the *New Edition of the Complete Works,* series 1, vol. 17 (Budapest: Editio Musica Budapest, 1983).

As the principal source for the orchestral interlude, the editor has used the last source Liszt is known to have corrected: the proofs prepared by his publisher Kahnt (GSA Depositum Hoffmann 5b). They consist of fifty sheets paginated 3–52 and are stamped with the date 1. Mai 84. The title reads: "Salve Polonia" Interludium des Oratoriums "Stanislaus."

The edition of the psalm, "De profundis," is based on the printer's manuscript (GSA Depositum Hoffmann 15a) prepared by August Göllerich under Liszt's supervision and delivered to Kahnt on 13 June 1886. There are seven leaves paginated 1–13. Each page contains 12 staves and measures 26.7 cm in width and 34.7 cm in length. The title reads: Der 129. Psalm: / "De profundis." Göllerich included an alternate, German-language vocal part (in red ink), which is not included in this edition. Also not included are the double bar-lines that he used to indicate changes of forces between systems and the slurs used to mark vocal melismas.

The principal source for the final chorus is the printer's manuscript of the orchestral score (GSA Depositum Hoffmann 5c) prepared by August Göllerich as a clean copy of Liszt's autograph (GSA 60/B3r, of which only fragments survive). Liszt made corrections and additions (mostly in black ink) to the clean copy and submitted it to Kahnt on 13 June 1886. The instrumental parts beginning at *Poco a poco animato* are in an unidentified third hand. There are sixteen pages measuring 26.9 cm in width and 34.3 cm in length, with 20 staves per page. The title reads: Schluss=Chor mit Baryton-Solo.

Editorial Methods

The following aspects of notation have been standardized in preparing this edition: the order of instruments and voices; the placement of tempo and other written directives meant for the entire score; the placement of clefs, key signatures, and meter signatures; the spelling, orthography, and placement of expressive and dynamic markings (and their abbreviations); the use of double bar-lines before changes of key; the direction of note stems. All instrument names and references to instruments have been translated into English. Where Liszt used "Solo" merely to indicate the principal wind or bass instrument, the word is replaced by the numeral 1 (or the numeral 3 for the third horn). Redundant indications of the keys of transposing instruments have been removed, as have redundant indications of manner of performance (as in "pizz."). Most redundant accidentals have been omitted. Slurs have been extended to enclose ties except in cases where a single tie lies between two slurred phrases. Slur markings used to indicate groupettes (and not meant as phrasing slurs) have been replaced by brackets. Cross-staff stemming has been suppressed in the piano scores. The four choral voices have been assigned to separate staves even in those unison passages where they share staves in the source. In the second part of the interlude, clefs for the percussion instruments of indefinite pitch have been removed.

Editorial additions have been placed in brackets, except in the cases of slurs, ties, and hairpins (which are dashed) and letter dynamics (which are set in bold type rather than the customary bold-italic). Some editorial additions are derived from secondary sources, namely from the piano score (GSA 60/B3e) of the orchestrated numbers of scene 1, the printer's manuscript (GSA Depositum Hoffmann 5a) and published edition (plate number 2764) of the interlude, and the autograph fragments (GSA 60/B3r) and piano score (GSA Depositum Hoffmann 5d) of the final chorus. In the principal source of the interlude (GSA Depositum Hoffmann 4b), Liszt made corrections in black ink while someone else made corrections in lead pencil and blue pencil; the corrections by the unknown hand are bracketed.

Unbracketed additions include writing out abbreviations, realizing Liszt's instructions that one part should double another (e.g., where the bassoons are instructed to play "mit den Violoncelli" in mm. 8–22 of the orchestral introduction), realizing the sign that a measure duplicates the notation of the previous measure, underlaying each choral part with text in those homorhythmic passages where Liszt underlaid just one part, adding whole rests to empty measures, and adding the words "geteilt" and "zusammen" (or their Italian equivalents; see below) where separate stemming is the sole indication of divided strings.

It appears that Liszt checked the principal source of the final chorus, Göllerich's copy of the full score, less carefully than he did Göllerich's copy of the piano score, since several errors went undetected. These errors have of course been reported in the critical notes with the readings of the edition based on GSA 60/B3r.

For paired instruments sharing a single staff, common stemming is used where viable and where doing so does not diminish clarity. Opposing stemming is used wherever there are different note values and rest patterns between the two instruments. Any added slurs made necessary by a change to opposing stemming are not considered editorial and are therefore not dashed. Voicing numerals and *a 2* designations found in the source are retained unless they are redundant. Where these indications are added to express what is already expressed in the source by another means (as in specifying the upper part by notating it with upstems and having rests for the lower part or as in using double stems to indicate unison playing) they are not considered editorial and therefore are not bracketed. Other indications that are added editorially are placed in brackets. The indication "tuba tacet" has been replaced with an indication that the bass trombone is to play. All such voicing indications and indications of specific instruments playing (whether original or editorial) have been repeated as necessary with each page turn.

Throughout the orchestrated sections of scene 1, the German terms "geteilt" and "zusammen" are used to indicate where parts divide and re-unite, while in the first part of the interlude, the Italian terms "divisi" and "non divisi" are used. These differences in terminology have been allowed to stand (with the spelling of "getheilt" modernized to "geteilt"). However, the second part of the interlude uses "getheilt" to indicate divisions, and there the term "divisi" has been adopted instead to lend consistency to the interlude as a whole.

Liszt's use of slanted slashes to notate string tremolo and percussion rolls has been retained. It is understood that three slashes indicate an unmeasured tremolo or roll, whereas two slashes indicate a measured reiteration (as in the second part of the interlude, m. 327, or in the final chorus, m. 1) unless marked with the word "tremolo" (as in scene 1, full score, m. 163; although it is interesting to note that Liszt used eighth notes in the parallel passage of his piano-vocal score, GSA 60/B3e).

The original groupings of beamed notes have been retained except as reported in the critical notes. Where Liszt placed more than one part on a staff, rests have been added (in brackets) only where their absence might create difficulties in reading. Grace notes are reproduced exactly as they appear in the source. The fingerings in the piano scores are Liszt's.

The principal sources for the music are also the principal sources for the sung texts. Spelling in the texts has not been modernized. Liszt tended to capitalize second-person pronouns and each line of verse in the text underlay, but since he did so inconsistently, these practices have not been retained. The capitalization of every word in the text of the final chorus has not been maintained.

The source for punctuation in the orchestrated numbers of scene 1 is a copy of the libretto in Adelheid von Schorn's hand (GSA 60/B3a). Since there is no punctuation in the text of the aria (as is often the case in Liszt's autographs), and since the text differs from all extant versions of the libretto, the editor has seen fit to provide it with his own punctuation. This has been done in the text of the final chorus as well, which also lacks punctuation in the source; the exclamation points were added to make the acclamatory nature of "Salve Polonia" clear. Where it exists, source punctuation has been regularized. In the text of the libretto (see appendix), periods after headings and character names have been removed.

Critical Notes

These notes describe the principal sources where they differ from the edition in ways not accounted for by the above statement of editorial methods. The following abbreviations are used: Stan. = Stanislaus; Mu. = Des Bischofs Mutter; Bol. = Boleslaw; T = Tenor; B = Bass; Picc. = Piccolo; Fl. = Flute; Ob. = Oboe; Cl. = Clarinet; Bn. = Bassoon; Hn. = Horn; Tpt. = Trumpet; T. Trb. = Tenor Trombone; B. Trb. = Bass Trombone; Tb. = Tuba; Timp. = Timpani; Pn. = Piano; Org. = Organ; Vn. = Violin; Va. = Viola; Vc. = Violoncello; Cb. = contrabass, r.h. = right hand; l.h. = left hand; m(m). = measure(s). Notes are numbered consecutively within a measure; where it is necessary to count notes sounding simultaneously, these are numbered from bottom to top. Pitches are indicated by the system in which middle C = c'.

Scene 1, Full Score

M. 6, Va., slur begins with note 1 (not with m. 5, note 1).   Mm. 17–20, Vn. 1, slur beginning in m. 17 ends at m. 20, note 1; additional slur in m. 20 from note 1 to note 5.

Mm. 17–20, Vn. 2, slur beginning in m. 17 ends at m. 20, note 4. M. 47, Hn. 1–2, the marking *a 2* is the editor's; Liszt wrote "2 Hörner" before the system that begins (in the source) at m. 49. M. 48, Bn. 1–2, measure repeat sign only refers to beats 2–3 of m. 47. M. 92, *a tempo* indication above Vn. 1 staff. M. 107, Bn. 1–2, no change of key signature. Mm. 132–42, sporadic staccato dots in Vc. (mm. 132–33), Vn. 2 (m. 138), and Vn. 1 (m. 139). Mm. 168–71, Cb., slur extends from m. 168, note 2, to the chord at the start of m. 171. Mm. 191–212, Timp. has key signature of one flat (so that flats on staff in mm. 191–94 are absent). M. 326, Stan., text reads "Der." Mm. 338–39, Stan., text reads "anbegehrt." M. 407, Bn. 1–2, note 2 is quarter note. Mm. 422–28, ending in E minor differs from piano score (GSA 60/B3e) which ends in E major with G♯s instead of G♮s.

Scene 1, Aria

M. 24, Pn., l.h., chords 4–9 are continuously beamed. M. 25, Pn., r.h., chords 1–2 are beamed together; l.h., chords 1–9 are continuously beamed. Mm. 35–188, Liszt wrote above m. 35, "Von hier an alles in 6/4 ausschreiben—bis auf 'als Zeuge der Gerechtigkeit' "; apparently he intended either to double the note values or to remove every other barline. M. 76, Pn., r.h., beam missing. Mm. 82–85, 97–100, and 101–4, Mu., text reads "Polenslande." M. 109, Pn., r.h., note 2 lacks augmentation dot; l.h., note 1 lacks augmentation dot. M. 129, Pn., l.h., notes lack augmentation dots. M. 159, Pn., r.h., note 3 lacks augmentation dot. M. 201, Pn., tremolos are marked with an "18." M. 225, Pn., l.h., note 1 lacks augmentation dot. M. 249, Mu., note lacks augmentation dot. M. 250, Mu., half note is dotted. M. 268, Mu., note lacks augmentation dot. M. 297, Pn., l.h., note 3 lacks augmentation dot. M. 323, Pn., l.h., note 2 lacks augmentation dot. Mm. 323–28, Pn., some notes intended for r.h. are written in the lower staff. M. 325, Pn., r.h., note 2 lacks augmentation dot; l.h., note 2 lacks augmentation dot.

Polonaise 1

M. 72, l.h., notes 1–2 lack augmentation dots. M. 80, l.h., notes 1–2 lack augmentation dots. M. 108, r.h., notes 7–9 lack augmentation dots; l.h., notes 7–9 lack augmentation dots. M. 109, r.h., notes 1, 3, and 7 lack augmentation dots. M. 115, l.h., note 7 is e'; note 10 (d') is written above the lower staff in bass clef but with the ledger line mistakenly placed above the note (the other notes of the chord appear in the upper staff); note 17 is e'; indication to repeat mm. 114–15 causes reports to apply again in m. 117. M. 119, r.h., note 8 lacks augmentation dot.

Polonaise 2

M. 29, r.h., beam lacking in lower part. Mm. 29–36, 53–60, 77–100, 125–32, 149–72, and 197–212, l.h., note values in the lower part are inconsistent (sometimes eighths, sometimes quarters), and sometimes there are eighth rests placed in the gaps of the upper part. M. 55, l.h., beam lacking in third beat. M. 70, l.h., note 9 is e♭'. M. 74, l.h., stems and beams lacking in lower part of second and third beats. Mm. 94, 96, 166, and 168, r.h., note 22 is f'''. Mm. 101, 102, 103, 104, 106, 173, 174, 175, 176, and 178, r.h., note 3 lacks augmentation dot. Mm. 107 and 179, trumpets, notes lack augmentation dots. Mm. 126 and 198, l.h., beam lacking in third beat. Mm. 129 and 201, r.h., *8va* indication begins with chord 5 (which is therefore notated an octave lower). M. 221, l.h., note 2 lacks augmentation dot. M. 249, r.h., repeated chords separately notated as beamed eighths. M. 282, l.h., stem lacking on chord 4. Mm. 289–90 and 295–96, l.h., upper part has quarter rests on the downbeats. M. 298, r.h., beam lacking. M. 302, r.h., beam lacking. Mm. 302–4, l.h., beams lacking. M. 340, r.h., notes lack augmentation dots. M. 342, r.h., notes lack augmentation dots; l.h., note 2 lacks augmentation dot.

Scene 4, Interlude, Part I

M. 39, Bn. 1–2, chords 2–3 have crescendo hairpin. M. 42, Cl. 1–2, quarter-note chord. M. 51, Vc., hairpin begins with note 1 (not with m. 50, note 2). M. 65, Va., note 5 has staccato dot. M. 77, Va. and Vc. have *dol.* (copyist's errors; Liszt wrote "sol," meaning the pitch G). M. 133, Tb., note 1 lacks augmentation dot. M. 140, Cl. 2, note 4 is e♮". M. 148, Bn. 2, instruction reads "un poco marcato il 2 Fag." M. 148, Vn. 1, flag lacking on chord 3. M. 157, Bn. 1–2, note 5 has augmentation dot. M. 169, Bn. 1–2, chords 2 and 4 have staccato dots.

Scene 4, Interlude, Part II

M. 14, instruction appears as "In vier Vierteln zu taktiren" and is set as an asterisked footnote. M. 39, instruction appears as "In vier Viertel taktiren" above the strings. M. 61, Vn. 1, note 3 is a♭". M. 106, Ob. 2, notes 2–3 are a'. M. 108, B. Trb. and Tb. have *f stacc.* (instead of in m. 107). M. 111, Picc., dynamic reads "mezza forte." M. 127, Hn. 1–2, chord has staccato dot. M. 228, Ob. 1–2 have *p*. M. 231, Vc., the chord is notated as f♯ + d♯'; but twice—once on the staff and again in the margin—Liszt wrote the letters *h* and *d*. Mm. 241–42, Fl. 1–2, each bar slurred separately. Mm. 241–42, Cl. 1–2, each bar slurred separately since in m. 242 the notes are engraved an octave higher (with no *8va*). Mm. 256, 258, and 260, Cb., repeated notes written as measured tremolo (dotted quarter note with two slashes). M. 264, instruction appears as "In vier Vierteln taktiren" at the bottom of the score. M. 312, Va., slur on notes 1–2 (both Bs). M. 315, Va., additional slur on notes 4 and 6 (both F♯s). Mm. 316 and 322, Va., slur on notehead side. M. 320, Timp., note 2 is quarter note. M. 328, Timp. has whole rest. Mm. 329–30, Timp., identical to mm. 332–33. M. 333, Hn. 1 and Hn. 3, note 4 is e"; Tpt. 1, note 2 is e". M. 336, Picc., note 6 has staccato dot. M. 337, Fl. 1, note 2 is g♯". M. 354, Va., additional slur on notes 2 and 4 (both Bs). M. 357, Vn. 2, note 4 is a'. M. 367, Ob. 2, notes 2–3 are f♯". M. 372, Hn. 1–2, note 1 has staccato dot.

Scene 4, Psalm

Mm. 37–45 and 96–104, the nine measures of the chorus are pasted over what had been seven measures, so that in each case the organ part has two fewer measures than the chorus.　M. 44, T, stem lacking on note 1.　M. 44, B2, stem lacking on note 3.　M. 45, Org. has fermata. Mm. 223–25, Org., r.h., m. 223 and mm. 224–25 slurred separately.　Mm. 229–30, Org., r.h. and l.h., each bar slurred separately.　Mm. 252–55, Bol., the settings of "ipse" (mm. 252–53) and "redimet" (mm. 254–55) slurred separately.

Scene 4, Chorus

Mm. 1–34, Fl. 1–2, part lacks four-sharp key signature, lacks natural signs in mm. 19–22 and 27–30, and has sharps on notes in mm. 23 and 31.　Mm. 9–11, T, slur beginning in m. 9 ends at m. 10, chord 3; additional slur in m. 10 from chord 3 to chord 4.　M. 15, Hn. 1–2 and Hn. 3–4 have notes shown in m. 16 of edition, and in m. 16, have whole rests shown in m. 15 of edition.　Mm. 20 and 76, Hn. 1, instruction reads "1ter Horn espressivo." Mm. 23 and 79, *tremol.* indication above Vn. 1 staff.　Mm. 23–24, 31–32, 79–80, and 87–88, Bol., whole note tied to quarter note.　Mm. 24, 32, 80, and 88, B1, note 2 is a. Mm. 25 and 81, Cl. 1, note is g'.　Mm. 38 and 94, Cl. 1, notes 2 and 6 are g'; Cl. 2, notes 3 and 5 are g'.　M. 39, Bol., slur begins (not in m. 38).　Mm. 41–42, Bol., notes of d♯, d♯, d♯ differ from piano score (GSA Depositum Hoffmann 5d) which has d♯, c♮, c♮.　Mm. 42 and 98, Vc., note 1 is a.　Mm. 43 and 99, Cl. 2, note has flag of eighth note.　M. 50, Fl. 1–2, Ob. 1–2, and Cl. 2, note 2 lacks augmentation dot.　Mm. 59–60, T 1–2, slur extends to m. 60, chord 1 (not to chord 2).　M. 65, Vn. 2, on the second beat the lower part has the pitch c♯'.　M. 68, T, slur begins with chord 2 (not with chord 3).　M. 73, Vn. 2, on the second beat the lower part has the pitch a.　M. 73, Va., quarter-note a, quarter-note b, half-note d♯'; all with tremolo. M. 75, Vn. 2, whole-note c♮' with tremolo (as in mm. 76–78).　Mm. 75–90, Fl. 1–2, part cancels four-sharp key signature in m. 75, lacks signature in mm. 75–90, lacks natural signs in mm. 75–78 and 83–86, and has sharps on notes in mm. 79 and 87.　M. 96, Bol., slur begins with note 1 (not with note in m. 94).　M. 101, Vn. 2, note 2 is f♮'.　Mm. 133–34, Hn. 3–4, repeated chords written as measured tremolo (whole notes with one slash).　Mm. 136 and 138, Hn. 3–4, whole notes only (with no slash). M. 145, T. Trb. 1–2, chord 1 is doubly dotted.　Mm. 145–48, 152, 156–59, and 166–67, Timp., rolls notated with *tr* indications and wavy lines.　Mm. 156–59, T. Trb. 1 and T. Trb. 2, note 1 is doubly dotted.　Mm. 157–59, Fl. 1–2 and Cl. 1–2, *segue* indication and dotted half notes with 3s indicate that repeated triplet quarter notes are to continue; these have been written out, with the notation applied editorially to Ob. 1–2.　M. 168, Org., r.h., chord is e' + g♯' + e" + g♯"; ties alone are used in mm. 158–67 to indicate that the chord of mm. 156–57 (g♯' + b' + e" + g♯") should be continued, but that chord is changed as noted in m. 168.

Appendix
Libretto, Final Revision (1883), GSA 60/B3b

St. Stanislaus

I. Bild

Der Schrei der Bedrückten
(Auf dem Berg Wawel vor den Thüren der Kathedrale.)
VOLK
Weh uns! Der Schmerzen Schale voll zum Rande!
Tyrann, dein Todesblick herrscht ob dem Lande,
Sowie ein Unheilstern am Firmament
Mit blut'ger Flammenruthe drohend brennt!
5 Dein Hauch verlöscht der Freiheit golden[es] Licht.
Das Zünglein an des Rechtes W[a]age spricht
Gehorsam nach, was deine Zunge lehrt.
Dein Wink gilt als Gesetz für Faust und Schwert,
In wilder Gier mit Schaaren deiner Würger
10 Raubst Weib und Tochter du dem stillen Bürger,
Und nimmst die Räuber schützend auf als Wirth—
Uns schützt der Bischof nur, der heil'ge Hirt.

(Der Bischof erscheint in den geöffneten Thüren der Kathedrale.)
BISCHOF
Kindlein, was weinet ihr?
　Was ist geschehen?

EINE STIMME
15 Sieh' uns ins Auge nur,
　Wirst uns verstehen!

EINE ANDERE STIMME
Mir haben all mein Gut
　Flammen verheeret.

EINE MUTTER
Mir ward mein Kind entführt—
20 　Weh!—und entehret.

EIN GREIS
Schmachtend mein Enkel liegt
　Schuldlos in Ketten.

RITTER
(Eilt herbei und kniet vor dem Bischof.)
Vater, nur du kannst noch
　Helfen und retten!
25 Boleslaw riss mein Weib

Scene 1

The Cry of the Oppressed
(At Castle Wawel before the doors of the cathedral.)
PEOPLE
Woe! Our cup of sorrows full to the rim!
Tyrant, your deadly eye rules over the land,
As a disastrous star in the firmament
Threateningly burns with flaming, blood-red tail!
Your breath extinguishes the golden light of freedom.
The scales of justice tip
In obedience to your word.
The wave of your hand is law for fist and sword;
In wild lust with bands of your stranglers,
You rob the peaceful subject of his wife and daughter,
And you receive and shelter robbers—
The bishop alone protects us, the holy shepherd.

(The bishop appears in the opened doors of the cathedral.)
BISHOP
My children, why do you weep?
　What has happened?

A VOICE
Just look in our eyes,
　And you will understand!

ANOTHER VOICE
Flames have laid waste
　All my property.

A MOTHER
My child was taken from me—
　Woe!—and dishonored.

AN OLD MAN
My grandson languishes,
　Guiltless, in chains.

KNIGHT
(Approaches in haste and kneels before the bishop.)
Father, only you can still
　Help and save us!
Boleslaw snatched my wife

Räub'risch von dannen.
Scheint noch der lichte Tag?
Schmettert kein Donnerschlag
    Auf den Tyrannen?
	Away, like a robber.
	Shines yet the light of day?
	Does no thunder crash
	    On the tyrant?

CHOR DER FRAUEN / CHORUS OF WOMEN

30 Mutter der Waisen! Du Pfleg'rin der Armen! — Mother of orphans! You guardian of the poor!
    Krone der Frauen! — Crown of women!
Schlug um dich, Vöglein, der Weih' ohn' Erbarmen — Little bird, did the kite without mercy
    Gierig die Klauen? — Greedily wrap its claws around you?

BISCHOF / BISHOP

Zum König eil' ich, Gottes Wort mein Schwert! — I will hasten to the king, God's word my sword!
35 Ich schaff' euch Recht und Ende euren Klagen. — I will bring about justice and the end of your laments.
Die Hölle sei in ihm auf's Haupt geschlagen, — May hell in him be fully vanquished,
Dass nach des Kreuzes Frieden er begehrt: — So that he may desire the peace of the cross:
Er soll nicht länger Gott zu trotzen wagen. — No longer shall he dare to defy God.

CHOR / CHORUS

Beschütz' uns Vater! Einzig in der Welt — Protect us, Father! Our only protection in the world
40 Verdanken Schutz wir deinem Hirtenstabe. — Is your shepherd's crook.
Wenn blut'ge Tyrannei den Sieg behält, — If bloody tyranny should triumph,
Dann suchen wir den letzten Schutz im Grabe. — Then we will seek ultimate protection in the grave.

BISCHOF / BISHOP

Wer in das Grab sinkt für Gerechtigkeit, — Those who sink into the grave for justice
Erhebt sich d'raus zu Himmelsherrlichkeit. — Will rise from there to heavenly glory.

ERZPRIESTER / ARCHPRIEST

45 Und selig ist, wer hier Verfolgung leidet, — And blessed are those who suffer persecution here,
Weil er die Himmelskrone sich erstreitet. — For they gain the crown of heaven.

BISCHOF / BISHOP

O hoffet noch, ihr Kindlein, hoffet! — Oh retain hope, my children, hope!
Sehnsüchtig Flehen wird erhört: — Yearning supplication is heard:
Stets ist des Vaters Herz euch offen, — The Father's heart is ever open to you,
50 Sein Arm des Bösen Macht zerstört. — His arm destroys the power of evil.

MUTTER DES BISCHOFS / MOTHER OF THE BISHOP

Der Herr gebeut den Königen: Ihr herrschet, — The Lord commands kings: you rule
Auf dass Gerechtigkeit hienieden sei. — That justice might be here below.

BISCHOF / BISHOP

Und ich will an die heilige Pflicht ihn mahnen, — And I will remind him of the holy duty
Dem Volke Schutz sein gegen Tyrannei. — To be protection for the people against tyranny.

MUTTER DES BISCHOFS / MOTHER OF THE BISHOP

55 So geh, mein Sohn! Du bist des Volkes Hirt, — So go, my son! You are the people's shepherd,
Vor ihn, der sein Verderber ist, tritt hin! — Take your stand before him, who is its ruiner!
Zeig' ihm, wie weit vom Heilesweg er irrt, — Show him how far he strays from the way of salvation,
Mit Gottes Wort erschütt're seinen Sinn! — Shake his senses with the word of God!
Gerührt heißt er den Frieden heim dich tragen, — If he is moved, you will return in peace,
60 Im Lande ringsumher verstummen alle Klagen. — And in the land all around every lament will fall silent.
Doch bleibt er hart bei seines Volkes Noth — But if he remains hardened toward his people's plight
Und raubt er grausam dir, mein Sohn, das Leben, — And cruelly robs you, my son, of life,
Als guter Hirt erleidest du den Tod, — As a good shepherd you suffer death,
Und ich geb' Gott zurück, was er gegeben. — And I give back to God what he has given.

<table>
<tr><td>

65 Zieh' hin als Held für Gott und Vaterland,
   Als starker Retter aus Tyrranenhand!

II. Bild

Das Königsmahl

(Ein Saal des Palastes festlich zum Banquet vorbereitet. Der König, die Großwürdenträger, Ritter, Krieger, Frauen.)

KÖNIG
Willkommen seid, ihr tapfre Herrn und Ritter,
Am Jahrestage jener blut'gen Schlacht,
Da ihr herangebraust wie Sturmesnacht,
Hinweggefegt gleich wildem Ungewitter
5 Die Mauern Kiews! Seid gegrüßt, ihr Sieger!
Willkommen all' ihr unbezwung'nen Krieger!

GEMISCHTER CHOR (Ritter, etc.)
Dem König Preis! Heil Boleslaw dem Kühnen!
Sein Lorbeer möge unverwelklich grünen!

KÖNIG
Der Siegestaumel jenes Tags berauscht
10 Mit süsser Trunkenheit mein Herz, vertauscht
Das Heute mit dem Einst: ich seh' euch ringen,
Wie Panther kühn auf Kiews Zinnen springen.

RITTER (gemischter Chor)
Dir König Ehre! Kiews Thor erbach
Nur deines Schwertes Blitz—wir drängten nach,
15 Wie Donner folgt dem Blitz. Doch du zum Sold
Gabst hin verschwenderisch uns Kiews Gold,
Die Schätze, Weiber, unermessne Beute!

EIN RITTER
O, dass zu neuem Kampfe du noch heute
Uns riefest! Rost an unsern Schwertern nagt—

KÖNIG
20 Sie werden wieder blank, seid unverzagt!
Gehöht die Polenmacht hat Kiews Fall
Doch bald bei neuem Kriegsdrommetenschall
Soll wachsen noch gewalt'ger unser Land!

KANZLER
Du zwangst die Veste, Herr, mit starker Hand;
25 Die Scharte noch an deinem Schwert beweist,
Wie man als kühnen Helden recht dich preist.
Doch nach des Kriegers Schwert ergreife mild
Des Königs Scepter nun, das Leiden stillt
In Friedensruh'! Lass, Herr, dein Volk gesunden,
30 Schlag' nicht mit neuem Krieg ihm neue Wunden!

KÖNIG
Willst etwa meistern du den Herrn im Land?—
Der Krieg, der Frieden ruht in meiner Hand.

</td><td>

Go forth as hero for God and Fatherland,
As strong deliverer from the hand of tyranny!

Scene 2

The Royal Feast

(A hall of the palace festively prepared for a banquet. The king, dignitaries, knights, warriors, women.)

KING
Welcome, brave lords and knights,
On the anniversary of that bloody battle
Where you roared up like a stormy night
And, like a wild thunderstorm, swept
The walls of Kiev away! Greetings, victors!
Welcome to all of you unconquered warriors!

MIXED CHORUS (Knights, etc.)
Praise to the king! Hail to Boleslaw the Bold!
May his laurel flourish unfading!

KING
The giddiness of victory from that day intoxicates
My heart with sweet drunkenness, and exchanges
Today for then: I see you wrestling,
Leaping like bold panthers on the battlements of Kiev.

KNIGHTS (mixed Chorus)
Honor to you, King! It was only the lightning of your sword
That broke open Kiev's gate—we followed close behind,
Just as thunder follows lightning. For our pay,
You lavished us with Kiev's gold,
The treasures, women, unmeasured booty!

A KNIGHT
Oh, that to new battle today you might
Call us! Rust gnaws on our swords—

KING
They will shine again, never fear!
The fall of Kiev elevated Polish might,
But soon, to fresh sounds of horns of war,
Our land shall grow mightier still!

CHANCELLOR
You conquered the fortress, Lord, with a strong hand;
The notches in your sword prove
How justly they praise you as a bold hero.
But after the warrior's sword, seize gently
Now the king's scepter; suffering subsides
In peacetime rest! Allow, Lord, your people to recover.
Strike not new wounds with new war!

KING
Do you wish, perhaps, to master the lord of the land?—
War and peace rest in my hand.

</td></tr>
</table>

KANZLER Du machtest Polen weit gefürchtet, groß, Doch ward es dessen froh? Ist Glück sein Loos?	**CHANCELLOR** You made Poland great and widely feared, But did this make Poland glad? Is happiness its lot?
KÖNIG 35 Das Glück ist unbezwung'ner Grösse Macht.	**KING** Happiness is the power of unconquered greatness.
KANZLER Doch Grösse giebt es, die zu Fall gebracht Gewalt'ge Reiche, Helden ungezählt—	**CHANCELLOR** But there is greatness which has caused the fall Of mighty empires, uncounted heroes—
KÖNIG Wer hat zum Sprecher dich hier auserwählt?	**KING** Who has chosen you as speaker here?
CHOR DER WÜRDENTRÄGER (auch FRAUEN) O König, höre ihn! Dein Volk verdirbt! 40 Indes du schwelgst, dein Volk vor Hunger stirbt.	**CHORUS OF DIGNITARIES (also WOMEN)** O King, hear him! Your people perish! While you indulge yourself, your people die from hunger.
KÖNIG Rebellen sind's, die solche Sprache wagen!	**KING** They are rebels, who dare to speak thus!
CHOR DER RITTER Rebellen sind's! Lass sie in Fesseln schlagen!	**CHORUS OF KNIGHTS** They are rebels! Have them thrown into fetters!
(In diesem Augenblick öffnen sich die Pforten, auf der Schwelle erscheint unbeweglich die Gestalt des Bischofs.)	*(At this moment the doors open, and the motionless form of the bishop appears on the threshold.)*
BISCHOF Ein unwillkomm'ner Gast wagt ungebeten Inmitten deines Festes einzutreten.	**BISHOP** An unwelcome guest dares, uninvited, To enter in the midst of your celebration.
KÖNIG (finster) 45 Der Freude gilt das Fest, du fliehst die Lust— Doch wann du jubeln willst aus voller Brust Beim Siegesfeste, das wir feiern hier Ob grimmem Feind: Willkommen! ruf ich dir.	**KING (darkly)** Joy is fitting to the celebration, but you shun pleasure— And yet, if you wish to rejoice lustily At the feast of victory that we celebrate here Over our fierce enemy, then I welcome you!
BISCHOF Noch and're Feinde giebt's, und dich zu retten, 50 Nicht um zu jubeln, kam ich.	**BISHOP** There are still other enemies, and to save you, Not to rejoice, did I come.
KÖNIG Feinde? Wie?	**KING** Enemies? How so?
CHOR DER RITTER Ergreift sie alle! Werfet sie in Ketten!	**CHORUS OF KNIGHTS** Seize them all! Throw them in chains!
KÖNIG Nun, Priester—wo sind Feinde? Nenne sie!	**KING** Now, Priest—where are enemies? Name them!
BISCHOF Des Priesters Amt ist, Unheil zu verhüten, Er warnt, doch nicht verrathen darf sein Wort. 55 Verwahrt die Pforten: Aufruhr sah ich brüten, Verzweiflung reisst zu raschen Thaten fort.	**BISHOP** It is a priest's duty to prevent mischief; He warns, but his word must not betray. Guard the doors: I saw rebellion breeding, Despair carries away to rash deeds.
KÖNIG Fort auf die Warten! Nieder lasst die Brücken! Besetzt das Thor! Die Schwerter lasst uns zücken!	**KING** Away to the lookouts! Lower the bridges! Hold the gate! Let's draw our swords!

CHOR DER RITTER Und keine Schonung! Mordet! Werft sie nieder! 60 Schlagt alle Köpfe ab der gift'gen Hyder!	**CHORUS OF KNIGHTS** And no mercy! Kill them! Crush them! Cut all the heads off the poisonous hydra!
KÖNIG Dir, Bischof, dank' ich. Lass zurück dich leiten!— Der leichte Sieg hilft größeren bereiten.	**KING** I thank you, Bishop. You may return!— An easy victory helps to prepare for greater ones.
BISCHOF Was sinnst du Herr? Nicht schmiede neue Ketten! Vor Frevel nur dacht' ich mein Volk zu retten.	**BISHOP** What are you thinking, Lord? Do not forge new chains! I only thought to save my people from sacrilege.
KÖNIG 65 *Dein* Volk! Du wagst vor mir ein solches Wort?	**KING** *Your* people! You dare to speak these words before me?
BISCHOF Nicht Stolz reisst mich zu dieser Rede fort: Des Volkes König du, doch ich sein Hirt, Der mahnt und warnt und retten will, was irrt.	**BISHOP** It is not pride that makes me speak these words: You are the king of the people, but I am their shepherd, Who admonishes and warns and will save those who stray.
CHOR DER RITTER Bei diesem Amt wird dich kein König hindern.	**CHORUS OF KNIGHTS** No king will hinder you in this office.
BISCHOF 70 Er thut es dennoch. Polens armen Kindern Bleibt taub sein Ohr und fremd sein Kriegerherz: Ihn rührt ihr Elend nicht, ihr stummer Schmerz, Er hört den Jammer nicht, ihr lautes Klagen.	**BISHOP** And yet, he does. Toward Poland's poor children His ear remains deaf and his warrior's heart cold: Their misery and mute pain do not move him, He does not hear the wailing, their loud lament.
CHOR DER RITTER D'rum kommst du selbst Empörung her zu tragen.	**CHORUS OF KNIGHTS** For this reason you come in person to carry revolt here.
KÖNIG 75 Nun seh' ich klar—der Kanzler hat's gezeigt— Nicht Jeder auch, der Polens Sprache spricht, Liebt Polens Ruhm, kennt Unterthanenpflicht.	**KING** Now I see clearly—the chancellor has shown us— Not all who speak the language of Poland Love Poland's glory, or know the duty of a Polish subject.
EINIGE RITTER (und FRAUEN) Der gute Diener vor dem Herrscher schweigt.	**SEVERAL KNIGHTS (and WOMEN)** The good servant keeps silence before the ruler.
BISCHOF So denken Russen—Polen nimmermehr! 80 Denn freie Mannen sind's, kein Sklavenheer.	**BISHOP** So think the Russians—but never again the Poles! For they are free men, not slaves.
KANZLER UND SCHATZMEISTER O hör' den Bischof! Gott hat ihn gesandt. Nicht Macht noch Schätze frommen uns'rem Land, Die Freiheit nur erblühet Polens Glück!	**CHANCELLOR AND TREASURER** Oh hear the bishop! God sent him. Neither might nor wealth benefit our land; Freedom alone brings good fortune to bloom in Poland!
KÖNIG (zum Bischof) Du hast geredet. Kehre zum Altare, 85 Noch giebt mein Wort dir sicheres Geleit.	**KING (to Bishop)** You have spoken. Return to the altar, My word still gives you safe-conduct.
BISCHOF Beachte wohl! Der König wird geweiht Mit heil'gem Öl, dass er das Recht bewahre, Des Volkes Schutz, nicht sein Bedränger sei.	**BISHOP** Take heed! The king is consecrated With holy oil, that he might preserve justice And protect—not afflict—the people.

CHOR DER WÜRDENTRÄGER (gemischt)
Die Freiheit gieb! Fort mit der Sklaverei!

KÖNIG (wüthend)
90 Verräther oder Thoren! Vor Gefahren
Vermag nur Schwertes Macht das Recht zu wahren,
Doch nimmermehr der Freiheit leeres Wort!
Nicht fauler Friede, Krieg ist unser Hort!

CHOR DER RITTER
Den König schmäht, wer jeden Muthes bar
95 Und träge flieht des rauhen Kriegs Beschwerde.

CHOR DER WÜRDENTRÄGER (gemischt)
Der Bischof sprach als Hirt für seine Heerde.

KÖNIG (ironisch)
Ist dieser Hirt so hochgesinnt, nun gar
Des Kanzlers altes Herz noch zu begeistern,
So edel, seinen König selbst zu meistern—
100 Weshalb doch meistert er mit gleicher Gluth
Sich selber nicht zuerst, wenn Waisengut
Er vorenthält und schnöde selbst verzehrt,
Und sich mit himmelschrei'nder Schuld beschwert?

CHOR DER WÜRDENTRÄGER (gemischt)
Unmöglich! Herr, wir stehen für ihn ein!

BISCHOF
105 Nicht Bürgen noch Vertreter sollt ihr sein!
(Zum König) Sprich, König, welcher Schandthat du mich zeihst!

KÖNIG
Erbschleicherei, wie du am besten weisst.
Petrowins Erbe solltest du verwalten.

BISCHOF
Er hat's zum letzten Heller treu erhalten.

KÖNIG
110 Die Zeugen?

BISCHOF
Braucht des Bischofs Wort noch Zeugen?

KÖNIG
Beim Richter—ja!

CHOR VON RITTERN
Das wird den Stolzen beugen!

BISCHOF (begeistert)
Der Zeugen braucht es? Wohl, ich will sie stellen,
Und kämen sie auch von der Hölle Schwellen,
Und müsste sie der Himmel selbst mir senden!
115 Gott wird die Klage nur zur Ehre wenden.

CHORUS OF DIGNITARIES (mixed)
Give freedom! Away with slavery!

KING (furious)
Traitors or fools! In the face of dangers,
Only the power of the sword can preserve justice,
So nevermore this empty word, "freedom"!
Not lazy peace, but war, is our refuge!

CHORUS OF KNIGHTS
The king is reviled by those who, uncourageous
And lazy, flee the burden of rough war.

CHORUS OF DIGNITARIES (mixed)
The bishop spoke as shepherd for his flock.

KING (with irony)
If this shepherd is so high-minded as
To inspire even the chancellor's old heart,
So noble as to master his own king—
Why does he not first master with the same fervor
Himself, when the property of orphans
He withholds and shamelessly consumes,
And he burdens himself with outrageous guilt?

CHORUS OF DIGNITARIES (mixed)
Impossible! Lord, we vouch for him!

BISHOP
You shall be neither surety nor advocate!
(To the king) Tell us, King, the foul deed of which you accuse me!

KING
Legacy-hunting, as you know best.
You were supposed to administer Petrowin's estate.

BISHOP
He received every last penny.

KING
The witnesses?

BISHOP
Does the bishop's word need witnesses?

KING
Before a judge—yes!

CHORUS OF KNIGHTS
That will humble the haughty!

BISHOP (passionately)
Witnesses are necessary? Very well, I will raise them,
Though they come from the threshold of hell,
And heaven itself must send them to me!
God will turn the charge to honor.

CHOR DER RITTER Nieder mit ihm! Er höhnt und spottet dein!	CHORUS OF KNIGHTS Down with him! He mocks and scoffs at you!
KÖNIG Noch schützt mein Wort ihn heute—haltet ein! Und morgen schlägt mit Schmach ihn das Gericht.	KING My word still protects him today—stop! And tomorrow judgment will strike him with disgrace.
BISCHOF Erscheinen werd' ich—König, zweifle nicht!	BISHOP I will appear—King, do not doubt it!
(Waffenlärm nähert sich, Rebellen dringen kämpfend ein.) BISCHOF 120 Unselige, ihr dient der Freiheit schlecht!	*(The din of weapons approaches, rebels fight their way in.)* BISHOP Wretches, you serve freedom badly!
(Der Bischof wird verwundet, die Rebellen entwaffnet.) CHOR DER RITTER Gefängnis, Tod sei fortan euer Recht!	*(The bishop is wounded, the rebels disarmed.)* CHORUS OF KNIGHTS From now on, prison and death will be your due!
KÖNIG Den Bischof hebt und tragt ihn zum Verband, Denn morgen waltet erst des Richters Hand! Hinweg die Wunden! Fort die todten Gäste— 125 Sie taugen schlecht zu uns'rem Freudenfeste! Zum Mahle jetzt! Des Weines Feuergluth Erwecke uns den alten Siegesmuth!	KING Lift and carry the bishop to be bandaged, The judge's hand will not preside until tomorrow! Off with the wounded! Away with the dead guests— They are badly suited to our joyful celebration! Now to the feast! May the fire of wine Awake in us our former spirit of victory!
(Verhallender Waffenlärm, Seufzer der Verwundeten. Festmusik. Finale.)	*(The din of weapons dying away, sighs of the wounded. Festive music. Finale.)*

III. Bild

Das Wunder der Auferweckung

(Kirchhof bei der Kirche in Krakau. Das Zelt des Königs von Rittern und Volk umgeben. Der König sitzt zu Gericht.)

Scene 3

The Miracle: Raising Petrus

(Cemetery by the church in Krakow. The tent of the king surrounded by knights and the people. The king sits in judgment.)

EINSIEDLER Hörnerton schallt! Purpurumwallt Auf der finsteren Stirn einen Strahl Von der schimmernden Polenkrone, 5 Düster das Antlitz und fahl, Boleslaw ragt.— Und verklagt Als ein Räuber fremden Gutes Naht der Bischof seinem Throne. 10 Seht den König, wilden Muthes Wie die Hand ihm zuckt ans Schwert! Tiefer Groll sein Herz verzehrt.	HERMIT Horn calls resound! Wrapped in folds of purple, On his dark brow, a ray of light From the gleaming crown of Poland, Gloomy his face, and pale, Boleslaw looms.— And accused As a robber, The bishop approaches his throne. See the king of wild spirit, How his hand twitches on his sword! Deep, stifled hatred eats at his heart.
CHOR DES VOLKES Bischof, den über Menschenseelen, Die in Sündenschuld irren und fehlen, 15 Gott als Richter gesetzt, Zuflucht aller Bedrängten und Armen, Welchem Richter ohne Erbarmen Nahest du wehrlos jetzt!	CHORUS OF THE PEOPLE Bishop, whom God has placed as judge Over human souls that, guilty of sin, Stray and err, O refuge for all the afflicted and poor, What a merciless judge You defenseless now approach!

KÖNIG (zum Bischof) Stanislaus, steh' Rede hier, 20 Wie du Petrus' Gut erworben, Dass dir mag dein Recht geschehn!	**KING** (to Bishop) Stanislaus, give here an account Of how you acquired Petrus's property, That justice may be served on your behalf.
BISCHOF Gottes Aug' hat es gesehn: Petrus nahm, eh' er gestorben, Für sein Dorf das Gold von mir.	**BISHOP** The eye of God saw it: Before Petrus died, he took From me the gold for his village.
KÖNIG 25 Kläger, seid entboten! Erben jenes Todten, Sprechet vor Gericht!	**KING** I summon the plaintiffs! Heirs of the deceased, Speak before the court!
DIE ERBEN (Brüder des Petrus) Du bezahltest jenes Dorf noch nicht, Hast es uns, den Erben, weggenommen, 30 Unser Bruder fuhr getäuscht zu Grabe! Gieb zurück uns die geraubte Habe! Nimmer kann der Waisen Gut dir frommen!	**THE HEIRS** (Brothers of Petrus) You have not yet paid for that village, You have taken it away from us, the heirs; Our brother went to the grave deceived! Give back to us the stolen property! The property of orphans can never be of use to you!
BISCHOF Ihr Armen, die ihr um vergänglich Gold Der Seele ewig Heil verkaufen wollt, 35 In Falschheit euch verhärtend und in Lüge! Der allgerechte Gott im Himmel weiß, Dass wahr ich sprach und nimmer euch betrüge.	**BISHOP** You wretched men, who, for ephemeral gold, Would sell the eternal salvation of your souls, Hardened in falsehood and in lies! The all-righteous God in heaven knows That I spoke truthfully and never would deceive you.
KÖNIG Lass Gott, und stelle Zeugen zum Beweis!	**KING** Enough about God. Present witnesses to testify!
BISCHOF König, du begehrst noch Zeugen?— 40 Vor des Richters Willen beugen Muss sich, wer verklagt ist. Flehen Zum Altare will ich gehen, Und den Zeugen vor Gericht Rufen dann, der für mich spricht.	**BISHOP** King, do you still want witnesses?— Before the will of the judge, he must bend Who is accused. In supplication I will go to the altar, Then call before the court the witness Who will speak for me.
KÖNIG 45 Zeugen?—Auf der Erde Wandelt keiner mehr, Schlafen in der Erde Ohne Wiederkehr.	**KING** A witness?—There are no more Who walk on the earth; They sleep in the earth, Never to return.
CHOR DER HÖFLINGE Magst Gebete lallen, 50 Auf die Knie hinfallen, Büßen, dich kastein— Ha, vergeb'nes Streben! Todten neues Leben Hauchst du nimmer ein!	**CHORUS OF COURTIERS** You may stammer prayers, Fall on your knees, Do penance, chasten yourself— Ha, vain striving! You will never breathe New life into the dead!

MUTTER DES BISCHOFS
55 Welch herbes Leid!
    Allgerechter,
Den dir ich geweiht,
	MOTHER OF THE BISHOP
	What harsh injury!
	    O All-righteous One,
	On him whom I consecrated to you,

	Meinen Sohn	On my son,
	Bewerfen mit Hohn	The despisers
60	Die Verächter.	Heap scorn.
	Die todten Zeugen	The dead witnesses
	Sie schlummern und schweigen	Slumber and keep silence
	In ewiger Ruh:	In eternal repose:
	So sprich denn du,	So speak then, you
65	Der Alles weiß,	Who knows all
	Was ist und war!	That is and was!
	Mach' offenbar,	Make it clear
	Dass frei vom Schuld	That he stands before you
	Vor dir er steht!	Free of guilt!
70	Steige voll Huld	A mother's prayer
	Der Mutter Gebet	Ascends, full of grace,
	Dein heilig Antlitz zu,	To your holy face,
	Allerbarmer du!	All-merciful One!

CHOR DER FRAUEN / CHORUS OF WOMEN

	Mutter, lass dein Trauern enden!	Mother, let your mourning end!
75	Engel wird der Herr ihm senden.	Angels the Lord will send to him.
	Sieh, aus seinem Auge bricht	See, already from his eye refracts
	Schon ein Strahl wie Sonnenlicht,	A ray like sunlight;
	In dem Antlitz hell es ruht	It rests bright on his face
	Wie der Morgenröthe Gluth!	Like the glow of dawn!

VOLK / PEOPLE

80	Seht, der Bischof eilt von hinnen—	Look, the bishop hastens away—
	Welch Beginnen! Welch Beginnen!	What a beginning! What a beginning!

PILGERIN / PILGRIMESS

	In die Kirche!—Weiter!—Weiter!	Into the church!—Onward!—Onward!
	Hoch das Herz, du Gottesstreiter!	Be heartened, warrior of God!
	Seht den Hirten, seht die Heerde,	See the shepherd, see the flock,
85	Wie sie nieder auf die Erde	How they fall to the ground
	Vor dem Kreuzesbilde fallen—	Before the image of the cross—
	Fester Glaube lebt in Allen!—	Firm faith lives in all!—
	Seht den Bischof sich erheben!	See the bishop rise!
	Seht die Glorie ihn umschweben!	See the glory hang about him!
90	Nun zur Gruft lenkt er den Schritt,	Now he directs his steps to the tomb,
	Und das Volk zieht betend mit.—	And the people, praying, go along.—
	Still das Gedränge,	The crowd is still,
	Verstummt die Menge	The multitude struck dumb
	In Schauder und Staunen!	With awe and astonishment!
95	Wie des Gerichte Posaunen	Like the trumpets of judgment
	Am jüngsten Tag erdrö[h]nen,	At the last day,
	Des Bischofs Worte tönen!	The bishop's words sound!

BISCHOF / BISHOP

	Im Namen Jesu, der erstanden,	In the name of the risen Jesus,
	Petrus, beschwört dich mein Stab:	Petrus, my staff conjures you:
100	Entringe dich den Todesbanden,	Wrest yourself from the bonds of death,
	Raffe dich auf aus dem Grab!	Snatch yourself from the grave!
	Felsengruft, zerbrich!	Tomb in the rock, break open!
	Todter, erhebe dich!	Dead one, get up!
	Petrus, erstehe!	Petrus, arise!

PILGERIN / PILGRIMESS

105	Horch, schauerliche Antwort tönt entgegen,	Listen, horrible answer in reply,
	Der Erde Tiefen tosend sich bewegen!	The depths of the earth, roaring, move!

BISCHOF Petrus, erstehe!	**BISHOP** Petrus, arise!
PILGERIN Der Stein erbebend auseinander bricht, Und in die off'ne Gruft strahlt Sonnenlicht!	**PILGRIMESS** The stone, shaking, breaks apart, And into the open tomb shines sunlight!
BISCHOF 110 Petrus, erstehe!	**BISHOP** Petrus, arise!
PILGERIN Des Sarges Deckel rasselnd springt empor: Aus Grabesnacht und Moderduft hervor Der Todte tritt!	**PILGRIMESS** The lid of the coffin, rattling, springs up: From sepulchral night and smell of decay, The dead man steps forward!
VOLK O Wunder! Staunt es an, Wie Gott es einst an Lazarus gethan!	**PEOPLE** Oh miracle! Gaze at it in wonder! As God once did to Lazarus!
BISCHOF 115 Dich, Petrus, hat mein Rufen von den Todten Als Zeugen vor des Richters Stuhl entboten!	**BISHOP** I called you, Petrus, from the dead To testify before the judge's seat!
PETRUS Ich folge dir, da mir der Herr gebot, Die Schmach zu wenden, die dich hier bedroht.	**PETRUS** I follow you, as the Lord commanded me, To turn away the disgrace that threatens you here.
BISCHOF Gebt Raum! Mein Zeuge naht!	**BISHOP** Make way! My witness approaches!
VOLK O Wunderthat!	**PEOPLE** Oh miraculous deed!
EIN HÖFLING 120 Das Blut erstarrt zu Eis in bangem Schrecken: Des Bischofs Ruf kann Todte auferwecken!	**A COURTIER** My blood freezes to ice in anxious fright: The bishop's call can raise the dead!
KÖNIG Kehrte wieder jetzt als Erdengast, Der seit Jahren hält im Grabe Rast? Trug nur ist's und Blendwerk!	**KING** Returns now as a guest of earth He who rested for years in the grave? It is only deceit and illusion!
CHOR DER HÖFLINGE Zauberei!	**CHORUS OF COURTIERS** Sorcery!
EIN HÖFLING 125 Horch, schon braust wie Meeressturm herbei Wildes Volk mit der erstand'nen Leiche!	**A COURTIER** Listen, already the tempestuous crowd, with the risen corpse, Blusters by like a storm at sea!
CHOR DER HÖFLINGE Horch—schon nah—und näher!—Herr, entweiche!	**CHORUS OF COURTIERS** Listen—already near—and nearer!—Lord, escape!
KÖNIG Nennt man mich den Kühnen, nur zum Scherz, Dass Gespenster mich zu schrecken meinen? 130 Wie mein Schwert ist auch aus Stahl mein Herz! Lasst den todten Mann vor mir erscheinen!	**KING** Am I named the Bold only in jest, That ghosts think they can frighten me? As my sword, so too my heart is made of steel! Let the dead man appear before me!

	ERSTER ERBE Wahrlich, Petrus tritt heran! Wagen wir ihn anzuschauen?	FIRST HEIR Truly Petrus steps near! Do we dare to look at him?
	ZWEITER ERBE Lasst uns fliehen! Welches Grauen!	SECOND HEIR Let us flee! What horror!
135	DRITTER ERBE Weh! Was haben wir gethan!	THIRD HEIR Woe! What have we done!
	BISCHOF (Petrus herbeiführend) Mit Thränen, König, habe ich gefleht, Dass Unrecht nicht und Reu' die Stirn dir beuge; Mit Leib und Seele Petrus vor dir steht, Ich rief ihn aus dem Grab, er sei mein Zeuge!	BISHOP (leading Petrus up) With tears, King, have I prayed, That injustice and remorse would not bend your brow; Petrus stands before you in body and soul, I called him from the grave to be my witness!
140	KÖNIG (zum Volke) So redet! Ist er's? Ihr habt ihn gekannt.	KING (to the People) So speak! Is he the one? You knew him.
	STIMME AUS DEM VOLK Er ist's, wie er im Leben vor uns stand.	A VOICE FROM THE PEOPLE He is, just as he stood before us in life.
	KÖNIG (zu Petrus) So rede, Zeuge, der im Jenseits wohnt: Ward dir das Dorf mit Goldespreis gelohnt?	KING (to Petrus) So speak, witness who lives beyond the grave: Were you compensated in gold for the village?
145	PETRUS Mich rief aus Grabesruhe Gottes Knecht, Dass ich von seinem Haupt Verläumdung wende! Mein war das Dorf und sein Besitz mein Recht, Die Recht gab ich für Gold in and're Hände: Der Bischof nahm das Gut, ich nahm den Lohn.	PETRUS God's servant called me from eternal rest, To turn away calumny from his head! The village was mine, and its possession was my right; I gave that right to another in exchange for gold: The bishop took the property, and I took the payment.
150	KÖNIG (zu den Höflingen) Verwünschtes Wort, Das ihn entsühnt, Der mich zu meistern Sich frech erkühnt.	KING (to the Courtiers) Accursed word Which justifies him, Who impudently presumes to master me.
155 160 165	BISCHOF Der Gotteshauch Verweht wie Rauch Der Feinde Droh'n, Der Frevler Hohn, Er weckt den Todten Und schickt als Boten Der Wahrheitskunde Ihn dir zur Stunde Aus Grabesruh, O König, zu. Dem Gotteszeugen Musst du dich beugen, Vom Truge dich trennen, Demüthig erkennen Mit Sonnenklarheit Des Gottes Wahrheit—	BISHOP The breath of God Blows away like smoke The threat of enemies, The scorn of evil-doers; It awakes the dead man And sends him as a messenger Of true tidings, At this hour, From eternal rest To you, O King. To God's witness You must yield, Part from deceit, In humility recognize, Clear as daylight, God's truth—

KÖNIG (emporfahrend) In dir? Nein—nimmermehr! 170 Fahr' hin, der du hierher Den Höllentrug entboten, Da!—(*er sticht Stanislaus nieder*) 　　　Folge deinem Todten!	KING (running up) In you? No—nevermore! Begone, you who summoned here The deceit of hell, There!—(*he cuts Stanislaus down*) 　　　Follow your dead man!

[IV. Bild]　　　　　　　　　　[Scene 4]

—Bußpilgerfahrt Boleslaws, den Reue ob seinem That ergriffen hat.—
—De profundis im Kloster Ossiach in Kärnthnen, wo Boleslaw unerkennt bis an sein Lebensende als niederer Laienbruder seine Sünden abbüßt.—
—Salve Polonia.—

—Penitential pilgrimage of Boleslaw, who has been seized by remorse for his deed.—
—"De profundis" at the monastery of Ossiach in Carinthia, where Boleslaw expiates his sins as a minor lay-brother, unrecognized till his life's end.—
—"Salve Polonia."—

　　　Ende des Oratoriums　　　　　　　　End of the Oratorio

Recent Researches in the Music of the Nineteenth and Early Twentieth Centuries
Rufus Hallmark, general editor

Vol.	Composer: Title
1–2	Jan Ladislav Dussek: *Selected Piano Works*
3–4	Johann Nepomuk Hummel: *Piano Concerto, Opus 113*
5	*One Hundred Years of Eichendorff Songs*
6	Etienne-Nicolas Méhul: *Symphony No. 1 in G Minor*
7–8	*Embellished Opera Arias*
9	*The Nineteenth-Century Piano Ballade: An Anthology*
10	*Famous Poets, Neglected Composers: Songs to Lyrics by Goethe, Heine, Mörike, and Others*
11	Charles-Marie Widor: *Symphonie I in C Minor*
12	Charles-Marie Widor: *Symphonie II in D Major*
13	Charles-Marie Widor: *Symphonie III in E Minor*
14	Charles-Marie Widor: *Symphonie IV in F Minor*
15	Charles-Marie Widor: *Symphonie V in F Minor*
16	Charles-Marie Widor: *Symphonie VI in G Minor*
17	Charles-Marie Widor: *Symphonie VII in A Minor*
18	Charles-Marie Widor: *Symphonie VIII in B Major*
19	Charles-Marie Widor: *Symphonie Gothique*
20	Charles-Marie Widor: *Symphonie Romane*
21	Archduke Rudolph of Austria: *Forty Variations on a Theme by Beethoven for Piano; Sonata in F Minor for Violin and Piano*
22	Fanny Hensel: *Songs for Pianoforte, 1836–1837*
23	*Anthology of Goethe Songs*
24	Walter Rabl: *Complete Instrumental Chamber Works*
25	Stefano Pavesi: *Dies irae concertato*
26	Franz Liszt: *St. Stanislaus*